What the Butler Saw

A PLAY IN TWO ACTS

by Joe Orton

SAMUEL FRENCH, INC.
45 WEST 25TH STREET NEW YORK 10010
7623 SUNSET BOULEVARD HOLLYWOOD 90046
LONDON TORONTO

ISBN 978-0-573-61777-5 Printed in U.S.A. #121

WHAT THE BUTLER SAW opened officially on Monday, May 4, 1970, at the McAlpin Rooftop Theater, McAlpin Hotel, New York City, after 8 previews.

CHARLES WOODWARD and MICHAEL KASDAN

by arrangement with

LEWENSTEIN-DELFONT PRODS. LTD.

AND H. M. TENNENT LTD.

Directed by Joseph Hardy

Production Designed by William Ritman

Costumes by Ann Roth

CHARACTERS

(*In Order of Their Appearance.*)

DR. PRENTICE .... *Laurence Luckinbill*

GERALDINE BARCLAY .... *Diana Davila*

MRS. PRENTICE .... *Jan Farrand*

NICHOLAS BECKETT .... *Charles Murphy*

DR. RANCE .... *Lucian Scott*

SERGEANT MATCH .... *Tom Rosqui*

The text that follows represents the official acting edition of this play for productions in the United States and Canada. The script, blocking moves and physical production notes have been prepared exactly from the New York production of the play.

This text is being printed with the permission of the Estate of Joe Orton and is not to be confused with a "reading" text of the play which is also available in the United States.

What the Butler Saw

ACT ONE

The consulting room of an exclusive, private psychiatric clinic. A spring day. Doors lead to main hall U. R., *the wards and dispensary* D. R. *Double doors* U. L. *lead to a hall and the garden off stage. Open closet with hangers and hooks* D. L. *above proscenium and just off stage. Desk, chairs, consulting couch upstage with curtains.*

DR. PRENTICE *enters briskly from the hall.* GERALDINE BARCLAY *follows him.*

PRENTICE. Take a seat. Is this your first job?

GERALDINE. Yes, Doctor.

PRENTICE. (*Puts on a pair of spectacles, stares at her. He opens a drawer in the desk, takes out a notebook. Picking up a pencil.*) I'm going to ask you a few questions. (*He hands her a notebook and pencil.*) Write them down. In English, please. (*He returns to his desk, sits, smiles.*) Who was your father? Put that at the head of the page. (GERALDINE *crosses her legs, rests the notebook upon her knee and makes a note.*) And now the reply immediately underneath for quick reference.

GERALDINE. I've no idea who my father was.

PRENTICE. (*Is perturbed by her reply although he gives no evidence of this. He gives her a kindly smile.*) I'd better be frank, Miss Barclay. I can't employ you if you're in any way miraculous. It would be contrary to established practice. You did have a father?

GERALDINE. Oh, I'm sure I did. My mother was frugal in her habits, but she'd never economize unwisely.

PRENTICE. If you had a father why can't you produce him?

GERALDINE. He deserted my mother. Many years ago. She was the victim of an unpleasant attack.

PRENTICE. (*Shrewdly.*) She was a nun?

GERALDINE. No. She was a chambermaid at the Station Hotel.

PRENTICE. (*Frowns, takes off his spectacles and pinches the bridge of his nose.*) Pass that large, leather-bound volume, will you? I must check your story. To safeguard my interests, you understand? (GERALDINE *lifts the book from the bookcase and takes it to* DR. PRENTICE. *Consulting the index.*) The Station Hotel? (*Opening the book, running his finger down the page.*) Ah, here we are! It's a building of small architectural merit built for some unknown purpose at the turn of the century. It was converted into a hotel by public subscription. (*Nods, wisely.*) I stayed there once myself as a young man. It has a reputation for luxury which baffles the most undemanding guest. (*Closes the book with a bang and pushes it to one side.*) Your story appears, in the main, to be correct. This admirable volume, of course, omits most of the details. But that is only to be expected in a publication of wide general usage. (*Puts on his spectacles.*) Make a note to the effect that your father is missing. Say nothing of the circumstances. It might influence my final decision. (GERALDINE *makes a jotting in her notebook.* DR. PRENTICE *takes the leather-bound volume to the bookcase.*) Is your mother alive? Or has she too unaccountably vanished? That is a trick question. Be careful—you could lose marks on your final scoring.

GERALDINE. I haven't seen my mother for many years. I was brought up by a Mrs. Barclay. She died recently.

PRENTICE. I'm so sorry. From what cause?

GERALDINE. An explosion, due to a faulty gas-main, killed her outright and took the roof off the house.

PRENTICE. Have you applied for compensation?

GERALDINE. Just for the roof.

PRENTICE. Were there no other victims of the disaster?

GERALDINE. Yes. A recently erected statue of Sir Winston Churchill was so badly injured that the special medal has been talked of. Parts of the great man were actually found embedded in my stepmother.

PRENTICE. Which parts?

GERALDINE. I'm afraid I can't help you there. I was too upset to supervise the funeral arrangements. Or, indeed, to identify the body.

PRENTICE. Surely the Churchill family did that?

GERALDINE. Yes. They were most kind.

PRENTICE. You've had a unique experience. It's not everyone who has their stepmother assassinated by a public utility. (*Shakes his head, sharing the poor girl's sorrow.*) Can I get you an aspirin?

GERALDINE. No, thank you, sir. I don't want to start taking drugs.

PRENTICE. Your caution does you credit, my dear. (*Smiles in a kindly fashion.*) Now, I have to ask a question which may cause you embarrassment. Please remember that I'm a doctor. (*Pause.*) What is your shorthand speed?

GERALDINE. I can manage twenty words a minute with ease, sir.

PRENTICE. And your typing speed?

GERALDINE. I haven't mastered the keyboard. My money ran out, you see.

PRENTICE. (*Takes the notebook and puts it aside.*) Perhaps you have other qualities which aren't immediately apparent. (*Pulls aside the curtains on the couch.*) Kindly remove your stockings. I wish to see what effect your stepmother's death had upon your legs.

GERALDINE. Isn't this rather unusual, Doctor?

PRENTICE. Have no fear, Miss Barclay. What I see before me isn't a lovely and desirable girl. It's a sick mind in need of psychiatric treatment. The body is of no interest to a medical man. A woman once threw herself at me. I needn't tell you that this is spoken in confidence.

She was stark naked. She wished me to misbehave myself. And, d'you know, all I was conscious of was that she had a malformed navel? That's how much notice I take of women's bodies.

GERALDINE. Please forgive me, Doctor. I wasn't meaning to suggest that your attentions were in any way improper. (*Takes off her shoes and stockings.* DR. PRENTICE *runs a hand along her legs and nods, sagely.*)

PRENTICE. As I thought. You've a febrile condition of the calves. You're quite wise to have a check-up. (*Straightens and takes off his spectacles.*) Undress. (*Turns to the desk and takes off his coat.*)

GERALDINE. I've never undressed in front of a man before.

PRENTICE. I shall take account of your inexperience in these matters. (*Puts his spectacles on the desk and rolls back his cuffs.*)

GERALDINE. I couldn't allow a man to touch me while I was unclothed.

PRENTICE. I shall wear rubber gloves, Miss Barclay.

GERALDINE. (*Is worried and makes no attempt to conceal her growing doubts.*) How long would I have to remain undressed?

PRENTICE. If your reactions are normal you'll be back on your feet in next to no time.

GERALDINE. I'd like another woman present. Is your wife available?

PRENTICE. Mrs. Prentice is attending a more than usually lengthy meeting of her coven. She won't be back until this evening.

GERALDINE. I could wait until then.

PRENTICE. I haven't the patience, my dear. I've a natural tendency to rush things . . . something my wife has never understood. But I won't trouble you with the details of my private life till you're dressed. Put your clothes on this. Lie on that couch.

(GERALDINE *unzips and removes her dress and shoes.* DR.

PRENTICE *puts dress on hanger and hangs it in* D. L. *closet. Puts shoes on closet floor.*)

GERALDINE. What is Mrs. Prentice like, Doctor? I've heard so many stories about her. (*Stands in her panties and bra.*)

PRENTICE. My wife is a nymphomaniac. Consequently, like the Holy Grail, she's ardently sought after by young men. I married her for her money and, upon discovering her to be penniless, I attempted to throttle her . . . a mental aberration for which I've never forgiven myself. Needless to say, our relationship has been delicate ever since.

GERALDINE. (*With a sigh.*) Poor Dr. Prentice. How trying it must be for you. (*Climbing on to the couch.*) I wish there were something I could do to cheer you up. (*Closes the curtains.*)

PRENTICE. (*Puts on a white surgical coat.*) Well, my dear, if it'll give you any pleasure you can test my new contraceptive device.

GERALDINE. (*Looks through the curtain and smiles sweetly.*) I'll be delighted to help you in any way I can, Doctor.

PRENTICE. (*With an indulgent, superior smile.*) Lie on the couch with your hands behind your head and think of the closing chapters of your favorite work of fiction. The rest may be left to me.

(GERALDINE *disappears behind the curtain.* DR. PRENTICE *goes to the drawer in his desk. Starts to unzip his trousers.* MRS. PRENTICE *enters from the hall. She is wearing a coat.*)

MRS. PRENTICE. Who are you talking to?

PRENTICE. (*Is surprised and angry at his wife's unexpected appearance. Flushing, guilty.*) I must ask you not to enter my consulting room without warning. You're interrupting my studies.

MRS. PRENTICE. (*Stares about the room.*) Well, who were you talking to? There's no one here. Have you taken up talking to yourself?

PRENTICE. I was dictating a memo to the head nurse. She's worried about her inability to control her bladder.

MRS. PRENTICE. Can urine be controlled by thinking of one's favorite work of fiction? Hers is *Tess of the d'Urbervilles,* you know?

PRENTICE. Whose?

MRS. PRENTICE. The head nurse.

PRENTICE. My theory is still in the planning stages. I'd rather not discuss it. Why have you returned so soon?

(DR. PRENTICE *turns his back and zips up his trousers.*)

MRS. PRENTICE. I arrived at my meeting to find the hall in an uproar. Helen Duncanon had declared herself to be in love with a man. And, as you know, the coven is primarily for Lesbians. I myself am exempt from the rule because you count as a woman. We expelled Helen and by that time it was so late that I spent the night at the Station Hotel. It's so difficult being a woman.

PRENTICE. Well, I'm sure you're the best judge of that. (*A BUZZER sounds from the wards.*) It's an emergency in Ward B. They need me in Ward B. I trust you'll have left by the time I return. (*He goes.*)

MRS. PRENTICE. You can come in now. (NICHOLAS BECKETT *enters. He is a hotel page and wears a page boy's uniform.*) I'm not asking for my handbag back, or for the money you've stolen, but unless my dress is returned I shall file a complaint with your employer. You have until lunchtime.

NICK. I've already sold the dress for a lump sum. I could get it back at a price. I've also found someone to take an option on the photographs.

MRS. PRENTICE. (*Stares.*) What photographs?

NICK. I had a camera concealed in the room.

MRS. PRENTICE. When I gave myself to you the contract didn't include cinematic rights.

NICK. I'd like a hundred for the negatives. You've got until lunchtime.

MRS. PRENTICE. I shall complain to the manager.

NICK. It will do you no good. He took the photographs.

MRS. PRENTICE. Oh, this is scandalous! I'm a married woman.

NICK. You didn't behave like a married woman last night.

MRS. PRENTICE. I was upset. A Lesbian friend of mine had just announced her engagement to a Member of Parliament.

NICK. You must be more careful in your choice of friends. Look, I could reconsider. I'd like to get out of the indecent photograph racket. It's so wearing on the nerves. Can you find me a worthwhile job? I had a hard boyhood.

MRS. PRENTICE. What kind of job do you want?

NICK. I'm an expert typist. I was taught by a man in the printing trade.

MRS. PRENTICE. (*Firmly.*) I'm willing to pay for the photographs, but I can't possibly recommend your typing.

NICK. I want a hundred for the negatives and the job of secretary to your husband!

MRS. PRENTICE. You put me in an impossible position.

NICK. No position is impossible when you're young and healthy.

PRENTICE. (*Enters.*) Who is he?

MRS. PRENTICE. I neglected to mention that having lost my handbag at the Station Hotel this young man was kind enough to drive me home on his motor bike.

PRENTICE. I see. Drinking so early? You'll be sodden before lunch.

NICK. Have you a family, sir?

PRENTICE. No. My wife said breast-feeding would spoil her shape. Though, from what I remember, it would've been improved by a little nibbling. She's an example of in-breeding among the lobelia-growing classes. A failure in eugenics, combined with a taste for alcohol and sexual intercourse, makes it most undesirable for her to become a mother.

MRS. PRENTICE. (*Quietly.*) I hardly ever have sexual intercourse.

PRENTICE. You were born with your legs apart. They'll send you to the grave in a Y-shaped coffin.

MRS. PRENTICE. (*With a brittle laugh.*) My trouble stems from your inadequacy as a lover! That's the reason for my never having an orgasm.

PRENTICE. How dare you say that! Your book on the climax in the female is largely autobiographical. (*Pause. He stares.*) Or have you been masquerading as a sexually responsive woman?

MRS. PRENTICE. My uterine contractions have been bogus for some time! (*She exits into hall.* NICK *follows her out.*)

PRENTICE. (*Looking after her.*) What a discovery! Married to a mistress of the fraudulent climax. It's no good. . . . It's no good lying there, Miss Barclay. My wife has returned.

GERALDINE. Will she be able to help with your examination?

PRENTICE. The examination is canceled until further notice. Get dressed!

MRS. PRENTICE. (*Re-entering.*) Has your new secretary arrived?

PRENTICE. (*Holds the underwear behind his back.* GERALDINE *is concealed by the curtain.*) Yes. I've got her particulars somewhere. (*Unable to conceal the underclothes behind his back, he drops them into a wastepaper basket.*)

MRS. PRENTICE. Have you ever given thought to a male secretary?

PRENTICE. A man could never get used to the work.

MRS. PRENTICE. My father had a male secretary. My mother said he was much better than a woman.

PRENTICE. I couldn't ask a young fellow to do overtime and then palm him off with a lipstick or a bottle of Yardley's. It'd be silk suits and Alfa Romeos if I so much as breathed on him.

MRS. PRENTICE. Try a boy for a change. You're a rich man. You can afford the luxuries of life.

PRENTICE. I can't possibly. I've already given Miss Barclay a preliminary interview. (*Takes* GERALDINE'S *dress from the closet and tries to sneak it over the top of the curtains.*)

MRS. PRENTICE. (*Turns and sees him with the dress.*) You must explain . . . (*In a surprised tone.*) What are you doing with that dress?

PRENTICE. (*Pause.*) It's an old one of yours.

MRS. PRENTICE. Have you taken up transvestism? I'd no idea our marriage teetered on the edge of fashion.

PRENTICE. Our marriage is like the peace of God—it passeth all understanding.

MRS. PRENTICE. Give me the dress. I need it.

PRENTICE. (*Reluctant.*) May I have the one you're wearing in exchange?

MRS. PRENTICE. I'm not wearing a dress. (*Slips off her coat. Under it she is dressed only in a slip.*)

PRENTICE. (*Cannot conceal his surprise.*) Why aren't you wearing a dress?

MRS. PRENTICE. (*Putting on* GERALDINE'S *dress.*) I'll tell you frankly and with complete candor. Please listen carefully and save your comments for later. (*Zips up the dress.*) My room at the hotel was small, airless and uncomfortable. A model of its kind. When I turned down the bed I noticed that the sheets were none too clean. I went to the linen closet, which I knew to be on the second floor, hoping to find a chambermaid. Instead I found a page boy, the one in fact who was just here. He enticed me into the closet and then made an indecent suggestion. When I repulsed him he attempted to rape me. I fought him off but not before he'd stolen my handbag and dress.

PRENTICE. It doesn't sound like the kind of behavior one expects at a four-star hotel.

MRS. PRENTICE. The boy has promised to return my

dress. He's sold it to a friend who probably intends using it at sex orgies.

PRENTICE. Do you realize what would happen if your adventures became public? I'd be ruined. The doors of society would be slammed in my face. Did you inform the authorities of this escapade?

MRS. PRENTICE. No.

PRENTICE. Why not?

MRS. PRENTICE. I saw in the boy a natural goodness that had all but been destroyed by the pressures of society. I promised to find him employment.

PRENTICE. What qualifications has he got?

MRS. PRENTICE. He can type.

PRENTICE. There aren't many jobs for male typists.

MRS. PRENTICE. Exactly. He's been depressed by his failure in business. That's why he took to rape.

PRENTICE. How do you hope to employ him? Is there a market for illegal entrance?

MRS. PRENTICE. I don't propose to lead him into a dead-end job. I want you to hire him as your secretary. He'll be back soon. You can check his credentials at your leisure. Where is Miss Barclay?

PRENTICE. She's upstairs.

MRS. PRENTICE. I shall inform her that the position is no longer vacant.

PRENTICE. Could I borrow one of your dresses for a while, my dear?

MRS. PRENTICE. I find your sudden craving for women's clothing a dull and, on the whole, a rather distasteful subject. (*Exits into the garden.*)

PRENTICE. Miss Barclay—the situation is fraught—my wife is under the impression that your dress belongs to her.

GERALDINE. (*Looks through the curtain.*) Can't we explain, as tactfully as possible, that she has made a mistake?

PRENTICE. I'm afraid that is impossible. You must be patient for a little longer.

GERALDINE. Doctor—I'm naked! You do realize that, don't you?

PRENTICE. Indeed I do, Miss Barclay. I'm sure it must cause you acute embarrassment. I'll set about finding you suitable clothing.

(*He turns to the wastepaper basket, and is about to remove the underclothing when* DR. RANCE *enters from the hall.* DR. PRENTICE *drops the clothing into the basket and puts the basket down.* GERALDINE *ducks behind the curtain out of sight.*)

RANCE. Good morning. Are you Dr. Prentice?

PRENTICE. Yes. Do you have an appointment?

RANCE. No. I never make appointments. I represent our government, your immediate superiors in madness.

PRENTICE. Which branch?

RANCE. The mental branch.

PRENTICE. Do you cover asylums proper or just houses of tentative madness?

RANCE. My authority is unlimited. I have the power to close your clinic on a moment's notice should I find it necessary. I'd even have sway over a rabbit hutch if the inmates were mentally disturbed.

PRENTICE. You're obviously a force to be reckoned with.

RANCE. Indeed I am, but I hope our relationship will be a pleasant one. I'd like to be given full details of your clinic. It's run, I understand, with the full knowledge and permission of the local hospital authorities. (*He looks behind the curtains.*) You specialize in the complete breakdown and its by-products?

PRENTICE. Yes, but it's highly confidential. My files are never open to strangers.

RANCE. You may speak freely in front of me, Prentice. Remember I represent the government. Now, is this your consulting room?

PRENTICE. Yes.

RANCE. What's down this corridor?

PRENTICE. The first door on the right is the dispensary and the doors at the end of the hall lead to the wards.

RANCE. Is your couch regulation size? It looks big enough for two.

PRENTICE. I do double consultations. Toddlers are often terrified of a doctor. So I've taken to examining their mothers at the same time.

RANCE. Has the theory received much publicity?

PRENTICE. I don't approve of scientists who publicize their theories.

RANCE. I must say I agree with you. I wish more scientists would keep their ideas to themselves. (*A piece of paper flutters from under the curtain. Picking up the paper.*) Is this something to do with you?

PRENTICE. It's a prescription, sir.

RANCE. (*Reading.*) "Keep your head down and don't make a sound?" (*Pause.*) Do you find your patients react favorably to such treatment?

PRENTICE. I can claim to have had some success with it.

RANCE. Your ideas, I think, are in advance of the times. Why is there a naked woman behind there?

PRENTICE. She's a patient, sir. I'd just managed to calm her down when you arrived.

RANCE. You were attacked by a naked woman?

PRENTICE. Yes.

RANCE. Well, Prentice, I don't know whether to applaud your daring or envy you your luck. I'd like to question her.

PRENTICE. (*Goes to the curtains.*) Miss Barclay, a gentleman wishes to speak to you.

GERALDINE. (*Looking through the curtain.*) I can't meet anyone without my clothes on, Doctor.

PRENTICE. (*Coolly, to* DR. RANCE.) Notice the obstinacy with which she clings to her suburban upbringing.

RANCE. Have you tried shock treatment?

PRENTICE. No

RANCE. How long has she been a patient?

PRENTICE. The committal order hasn't yet been signed.

RANCE. Fill it out. I'll sign it.

PRENTICE. That's not my usual procedure, sir, to certify someone before examining them.

RANCE. The government requires certification before examination. Young woman, why did you take your clothes off? Did it never occur to you that your psychiatrist might be embarrassed by your behavior?

GERALDINE. I'm not a patient. I'm from the Friendly Faces Employment Bureau.

RANCE. (*Over his shoulder to* DR. PRENTICE.) When did these delusions first manifest themselves?

PRENTICE. (*Returning with a document.*) I've been aware of them for some time, sir.

RANCE. (*To* GERALDINE.) Do you imagine that any businessman would tolerate a naked typist in his office?

GERALDINE. (*Smiles and, in a reasonable manner, attempts to explain.*) Dr. Prentice asked me to undress in order that he might discover my fitness for the tasks ahead. There was no suggestion of my working permanently without clothing.

RANCE. (*To* DR. PRENTICE.) I shall take charge of this case. It appears to have all the bizarre qualities that make for a fascinating thesis. (*Signs the document.*) Make the necessary entry in your register and alert your staff of my requirements. (DR. PRENTICE *tears the document in half as he exits to the dispensary.* DR. RANCE *turns to* GERALDINE.) Young lady, is there a history of mental illness in your family?

GERALDINE. (*Primly.*) I find your questions irrelevant. I refuse to answer them.

RANCE. I've just certified you insane. You know that, don't you?

GERALDINE. What right have you to take such high-handed action?

RANCE. Every right. You've had a nervous breakdown.

GERALDINE. I'm quite sane!

RANCE. Pull yourself together. Why have you been certified if you're sane? Even for a madwoman she's unusually dense. (DR. PRENTICE *enters from the dispensary, wheeling a hospital trolley. On it are a rubber mattress, a pillow and a sheet. Over his arm,* DR. PRENTICE *carries a white hospital nightgown.* DR. RANCE *takes this from him. He throws it over the curtain to* GERALDINE.) Put that on!

GERALDINE. (*To* DR. RANCE.) Oh, thank you. It will be a great relief to be clothed again.

RANCE. (*Draws* DR. PRENTICE *aside.* GERALDINE *puts on the nightgown.*) What is the background of this case? Has the patient any family?

PRENTICE. No, sir. Her stepmother died recently after a remarkably intimate involvement with Sir Winston Churchill.

RANCE. What of the father?

PRENTICE. He appears to have been an unpleasant fellow. He made her mother pregnant at her place of employment.

RANCE. Was there any reason for such conduct?

PRENTICE. The patient is reticent on the subject.

RANCE. I find that strange. And very revealing. Prepare a sedative.

GERALDINE. Please call a taxi, sir. I wish to return home. I haven't the qualities required for this job.

RANCE. Lie on that trolley. You're slowing down your recovery rate, Miss Barclay.

(DR. PRENTICE *forces* GERALDINE *to take a pill and he lifts her onto the trolley. He covers her with the sheet. She gasps and bursts into tears.*)

GERALDINE. This is intolerable! You're a disgrace to your profession! I shall ring the medical association after lunch.

RANCE. Accept your condition without tears and without abusing those placed in authority.

GERALDINE. Am I mad, Doctor?

PRENTICE. No.

GERALDINE. Are you mad?

PRENTICE. No.

GERALDINE. Is this "Candid Camera"?

PRENTICE. There is a perfectly rational explanation for what has taken place. Keep calm. All will be well.

(MRS. PRENTICE *enters from the garden.*)

MRS. PRENTICE. (*Anxious.*) Miss Barclay is nowhere to be found.

RANCE. She's under strong sedation and on no account to be disturbed.

PRENTICE. (*Nervous, gives a fleeting smile in* DR. RANCE's *direction.*) My wife is talking of my secretary, sir. She's been missing since this morning.

GERALDINE. I'm Geraldine Barclay. Looking for part-time secretarial work. I've been certified insane.

RANCE. (*To* MRS. PRENTICE.) Ignore these random reflections, Mrs. Prentice. They're an essential factor in the patient's condition. (*To* DR. PRENTICE.) Does she have the same name as your secretary?

PRENTICE. She's taken my secretary's name as her "nom-de-folie." Although morally reprehensible, there's little we can do legally, I'm afraid.

RANCE. (*Drying his hands.*) It seems a trifle capricious, but the insane are famous for their wild ways.

MRS. PRENTICE. I shall contact the employment agency. Miss Barclay can't have vanished into thin air. (*Goes into the hall.*)

PRENTICE. My wife is unfamiliar with the habits of young women, sir. I've known many who could vanish into thin air. And some who took a delight in doing so.

RANCE. In my experience young women vanish only at midnight and after a heavy meal. Were your relations with your secretary normal?

PRENTICE. Yes.

RANCE. Well, Prentice, your private life is your own affair. I find it shocking nonetheless. Did the patient know of your liaison with Miss Barclay?

PRENTICE. She may have.

RANCE. I see. A definite pattern is beginning to emerge. (*Returns to the trolley and stands looking down at* GERALDINE. *Takes a white coat from* DR. PRENTICE.) Under the influence of the drug you've just—oh, thank you—administered to Miss Barclay, she will be relaxed and unafraid. I'm going to ask you some questions which I want answered in a clear non-technical style. (*To* DR. PRENTICE.) She'll take that as an invitation to use bad language. (*To* GERALDINE.) Who was the first man in your life?

GERALDINE. My father.

RANCE. Did he assault you?

GERALDINE. No!

RANCE. (*To* DR. PRENTICE.) She may mean "Yes" when she says "No." It's elementary feminine psychology. (*To* GERALDINE.) Was your mother aware of your love for your father?

GERALDINE. I lived in a normal family. I had no love for my father.

RANCE. (*To* DR. PRENTICE.) I'd take a bet that she was the victim of an incestuous attack. She clearly associates violence and the sexual act. Her attempt, when naked, to provoke you to erotic response may have deeper significance. (*To* GERALDINE.) Did your father have any religious beliefs?

GERALDINE. I'm sure he did.

RANCE. (*To* DR. PRENTICE.) Yet she claims to have lived in a normal family. The depth of her condition can be measured from such a statement. (*To* GERALDINE.) Did your father's church sanction rape? (*To* DR. PRENTICE.) Some religions will turn a blind eye to anything as long as it's kept within the family circle. (*To* GERALDINE.) Was there a church service before you were assaulted?

GERALDINE. I can't answer these questions, sir. They seem pointless and disgusting.

RANCE. I'm interested in rape, Miss Barclay, not the aesthetics of cross-examination. Answer me, please! Were you molested by your father?

GERALDINE. (*With a scream of horror.*) No, no, no!

RANCE. The vehemence of her denials is proof positive of guilt. It's a textbook case!

PRENTICE. It's fascinating, sir, and the questions are cleverly put together. Do they tie in with known facts?

RANCE. That need not cause us undue anxiety. Civilizations have been founded and maintained on theories which refused to obey facts. As far as I'm concerned this child was unnaturally assaulted by her own father. I shall base my future actions upon that assumption.

PRENTICE. Perhaps there's a simpler explanation for the apparent complexities of the case, sir.

RANCE. Simple explanations are for simple minds. I've no use for either. I shall supervise the cutting of the patient's hair. (*Wheels* GERALDINE *into the wards.*)

(DR. PRENTICE'S *glance falls on to the wastepaper basket. He shakes out* GERALDINE'S *underclothes, takes her shoes from the closet.* MRS. PRENTICE *enters from the hall.* DR. PRENTICE *swings round, turns his back on her and walks away, bent double in an effort to conceal the clothing and shoes.*)

MRS. PRENTICE. The young man is here.

PRENTICE. Ohhhh.

MRS. PRENTICE. (*Alarmed by his strange conduct.*) What's the matter? (*She approaches.*) Are you in pain?

PRENTICE. (*His back to her, strangled.*) Yes. Get me a glass of water.

(MRS. PRENTICE *hurries into the dispensary.* DR. PRENTICE *stares about him in desperation. He sees a tall vase of roses. He removes the roses and stuffs the underclothing and one shoe into the vase. The second shoe won't go in. He pauses, perplexed. He is about to replace the roses when* MRS. PRENTICE *enters carrying a glass of water.* DR. PRENTICE *conceals the shoe under his coat.* MRS. PRENTICE *stares. He is holding the roses. He gives a feeble smile and presents them to her with a flourish.* MRS. PRENTICE *is surprised and angry.*)

MRS. PRENTICE. Here you are. Put them back at once!

PRENTICE. Ohhhh. (*The shoe slips and* DR. PRENTICE, *in an effort to retain it, doubles up.*)

MRS. PRENTICE. Should I call a doctor?

PRENTICE. No. I'll be all right.

MRS. PRENTICE. (*Offering him the glass.*) Here. Drink this.

PRENTICE. (*Backs away, still holding the roses and the shoe.*) I wonder if you'd get another glass? That one is quite the wrong shape.

MRS. PRENTICE. (*Puzzled.*) The wrong shape?

PRENTICE. Yes, the wrong shape.

(MRS. PRENTICE *stares hard at him, then goes into the dispensary.* DR. PRENTICE *tries to replace the roses in the vase. They won't go in. He picks up a pair of scissors from his desk and cuts the stalks down to within an inch or so of the heads. He puts the roses into the vase. He looks for somewhere to conceal the second shoe. He shoves it between the space on top of the books on the lower shelf of the bookcase. He sees the stalks on the floor and kneels down to clean them up.* MRS. PRENTICE *enters carrying another glass. She stops and stares.*)

MRS. PRENTICE. What are you doing now?

PRENTICE. (*Lifting his hands.*) Praying.

MRS. PRENTICE. This puerile behavior ill accords with your high academic standards. Here, drink this. The young man I wish you to engage as your secretary has arrived.

PRENTICE. Perhaps he'd call back later. I'm not up to seeing anyone just now.

MRS. PRENTICE. I'll see what he says. He's an impatient young man.

PRENTICE. Is that why he took to rape?

(*She hurries away into the hall.* DR. RANCE *enters from the ward.*)

RANCE. You'll have no trouble recognizing the patient, Prentice. I've clipped her hair within an inch of the scalp.

PRENTICE. (*Shocked.*) Was it quite wise to do that, sir? Is it in accord with the present enlightened approach to the mentally sick?

RANCE. Perfectly in accord. As a matter of fact I've published a monograph on the subject. I wrote it while studying at the psychic institute. My tutor advised it. A remarkable man. Having failed to achieve madness himself, he took to teaching it to others.

PRENTICE. And you were his prize pupil?

RANCE. There were some more able than I.

PRENTICE. Where are they now?

RANCE. In mental institutions.

PRENTICE. Running them?

RANCE. For the most part.

(MRS. PRENTICE *enters from the hall.*)

MRS. PRENTICE. (*To* DR. PRENTICE.) The young man insists upon punctuality. He'll give you five minutes.

PRENTICE. A prospective employee, sir. I'm afraid you must excuse me. He'll give me five minutes.

RANCE. Very well.

PRENTICE. It's useless to claim that Socialism has had no effect.

RANCE. Mrs. Prentice, is there no news of Miss Barclay?

MRS. PRENTICE. None. She's still missing. I've checked with the Employment Bureau. Their clients have strict instructions to call them immediately after an interview. Miss Barclay has failed to do so.

RANCE. A search party must be organized. (*To* DR. PRENTICE.) What have you in the way of dogs?

MRS. PRENTICE. A spaniel and a miniature poodle.

RANCE. Let them be unleashed! Geraldine Barclay must be found or the authorities informed.

MRS. PRENTICE. I'll contact the warden. He has charge of the gate and will know whether she left the building. (*Turns to go.*)

PRENTICE. No—don't do that. Miss Barclay is quite safe. I've just remembered. She's in the therapy workshop.

RANCE. (*Pause, surprised.*) Why did you keep the fact from us?

PRENTICE. It'd slipped my memory.

RANCE. Have you suffered from lapses of memory before?

PRENTICE. I can't remember.

RANCE. Your memory plays you false even on the subject of its own inadequacy?

PRENTICE. I may have had a blackout. I don't recall having one on any other occasion.

RANCE. You might have forgotten. You admit your memory isn't reliable.

PRENTICE. I can only state what I know, sir. I can't be expected to remember things I've forgotten.

MRS. PRENTICE. What's Miss Barclay doing in the therapy workshop?

PRENTICE. She's making white tarbabies for sale in color-prejudice trouble-spots.

(DR. RANCE *and* MRS. PRENTICE *exchange startled looks.*)

RANCE. You claim, Prentice, that you forgot your secretary was manufacturing these monstrosities?

PRENTICE. Yes.

RANCE. I can hardly credit it. Once seen, a white tar-baby is not easily forgotten. What was the object in creating these nightmare creatures?

PRENTICE. I hoped it might promote racial harmony.

RANCE. These hellish white mutations must be put out of their misery. I order you to destroy them before their baleful influence can make itself felt.

PRENTICE. (*Wearily.*) I'll get Miss Barclay to carry out your orders, sir. (*He goes out to the wards.*)

RANCE. The man's a second Frankenstein.

MRS. PRENTICE. I don't believe we've been introduced.

RANCE. I represent our government. The mental branch. I'm here to investigate your husband's clinic and I find his behavior gives me cause for grave disquiet. Are you convinced that his methods can result in the lessening of tension between the sane and the insane ?

MRS. PRENTICE. The purpose of my husband's clinic isn't to cure, but to liberate and exploit madness.

RANCE. In this he appears to succeed only too well. Never have I seen matters conducted as they are in this house. Read that.

MRS. PRENTICE. (*Reading.*) "Keep your head down and don't make a sound?" (*Handing it back.*) What does it mean?

RANCE. It's a prescription of your husband's. He's using dangerously unorthodox methods in his treatment of the insane.

MRS. PRENTICE. I must confess that only this morning my husband prescribed the reading of Thomas Hardy to cure a disorder of the bladder.

RANCE. Now, you see what I mean. Have there been other schemes besides this tarbaby scandal?

MRS. PRENTICE. Endless ones. His letters to the newspapers are legion. From his first letter at the age of 12 speculating on the nature and extent of Nazi propaganda, to his latest published a month ago, in which he calls gentlemen's lavatories the last stronghold of male privilege. What do you think, Doctor? Is he a genius or just a highly strung fool?

RANCE. As a psychiatrist your husband seems not only ineffective but also undesirable.

MRS. PRENTICE. (*Discovers* GERALDINE'S *shoe and looks at it in amazement.*) Oh!

RANCE. (*Pause.*) What is it?

MRS. PRENTICE. A shoe.

RANCE. Is it yours?

MRS. PRENTICE. No.

RANCE. Let me see it. (*She hands him the shoe. He turns it over in his hand. Looking up, after a pause.*) I must ask you to be honest with me, Mrs. Prentice. Has Dr. Prentice at any time given you cause to doubt his own sanity?

MRS. PRENTICE. (*Gives a quick gasp of fear, rising to her feet.*) He's a respected member of his profession. His work in all fields has been praised by numerous colleagues.

RANCE. Let me remind you, Mrs. Prentice, that radical thought comes easily to the lunatic.

MRS. PRENTICE. (*Pause.*) You're quite right. I've known for some time that all was not well. I've tried to convince myself that my fears were groundless. All the while I knew I was deceiving myself.

RANCE. (*Quietly.*) What first aroused your suspicions?

MRS. PRENTICE. His boorish attitude towards my mother. He used to call her up on the telephone and suggest painful ways of committing suicide. Worn out at last by his pestering, she took his advice.

RANCE. And more recently, say from this morning, has there been an increase in his condition?

MRS. PRENTICE. Oh, yes. Quite definitely, Doctor. He had no sympathy for me when I complained of being assaulted by a page boy at the Station Hotel.

RANCE. What was the object of the assault?

MRS. PRENTICE. The boy wanted to rape me.

RANCE. Did he succeed?

MRS. PRENTICE. No.

RANCE. (*Shaking his head.*) The service in these hotels is dreadful.

MRS. PRENTICE. And now he has developed a craving for women's clothes.

RANCE. (*Picking up* GERALDINE'S *shoe.*) This confirms your story. I can't doubt that what you've told me has great significance. We must also take into account his admitted lapse of memory, and the attempts to create alien forms of life. Say nothing of our suspicions. Fancies grow like weeds in the unhealthy soil of a sick brain. (DR. PRENTICE *enters Turning to him.*) Have you carried out my instructions?

PRENTICE. Yes.

RANCE. You guilty scientists will destroy the world with your shameful secrets. (*Takes* GERALDINE'S *shoe.*) Does this belong to your secretary?

PRENTICE. No. (*Pause.*) It's mine.

RANCE. (*Heavily, with irony.*) Are you in the habit of wearing women's footwear?

PRENTICE. (*Quickly, desperate.*) My private life is my own. Society must not be too harsh in its judgments. (*Tries to grab shoe from* RANCE. RANCE *won't let it go.*)

RANCE. Where is this secretary of yours? I've a few questions I'd like to put to her.

PRENTICE. I can't allow you to disturb her. She has work to do.

RANCE. I don't think you quite appreciate your position, Prentice. The powers vested in me by the government give the right to interview any member of your staff should occasion demand. (RANCE *dislodges shoe from* PRENTICE. *Thrusts it into his case.*) Where is Geraldine Barclay?

PRENTICE. She's in the garden.

RANCE. Ask her to step this way.

PRENTICE. She's making a funeral pyre for the tar-babies. It would be wrong to disturb her.

RANCE. Very well. I shall seek her out myself. You

may be sure, Prentice, your conduct won't go unreported! (*Goes to the garden.*)

PRENTICE. (*Turns on his wife.*) What've you told him?

MRS. PRENTICE. Nothing but the truth.

PRENTICE. You've been spreading it around that I'm a transvestite, haven't you?

MRS. PRENTICE. There was a woman's shoe hidden in the bookcase. What was it doing there?

PRENTICE. Why were you rooting among my books?

MRS. PRENTICE. I was looking for the clippings file. I showed it to Dr. Rance.

PRENTICE. You'd no right to do that.

MRS. PRENTICE. Are you ashamed of the fact that you write to strange men?

PRENTICE. There's nothing suspect about my relationship with the editor of *The Times*.

MRS. PRENTICE. Dr. Rance and I are trying to help you. We're not satisfied with your condition.

PRENTICE. Neither am I. It's impossible and you're to blame.

MRS. PRENTICE. (*Turns on* DR. PRENTICE *resentfully.*) Whose fault is it if our marriage is on the rocks? You're selfish and inconsiderate.

PRENTICE. (*He backs her against the desk and begins to unzip her dress.*) Your irresponsible behavior causes me untold anxiety. Your nymphomania knows no bounds.

MRS. PRENTICE. You've no psychological understanding of the difficulties I face.

PRENTICE. (*Her dress is off her shoulders.*) Unless you're very careful you'll find yourself in a suitcase awaiting collection!

MRS. PRENTICE. These veiled threats confirm the doubts I already have of your sanity.

(NICK *enters from the hall, carrying a dress on a hanger.*)

NICK. I'm tired of waiting, madam. I believe this is yours. Do you want it?

MRS. PRENTICE. (*With delight.*) My dress!

PRENTICE. A dress? I'll take that. (*Grabs the dress and hanger from* NICK.)

MRS. PRENTICE. I shall inform Dr. Rance of your theft of one of my dresses.

PRENTICE. Don't raise your voice.

NICK. If you'll hand over the money, madam, I'll let you have the photos. However, some guarantee of employment must be given before I part with the negatives.

PRENTICE. What's he talking about?

MRS. PRENTICE. He has in his possession a series of pornographic studies of me. He took them last night without my knowledge.

PRENTICE. I suppose I shall have to turn pederast to get you out of this mess. Take a biscuit from the barrel and retire to your room. (*He chases her out the hall door.*)

NICK. I'm sorry if my behavior last night caused your wife undue anxiety, but I've a burning desire to sleep with every woman I meet.

PRENTICE. That's a filthy habit and, in my opinion, very injurious to the health.

NICK. It is, sir. My health's never been the same since I went off stamp collecting.

PRENTICE. We have an overall moral policy in this clinic from which even I am not exempt. While you're with us as my secretary I shall expect you to show an interest in no one's sexual organs but your own.

NICK. I would miss a lot of fun that way.

PRENTICE. That is the purpose of the exercise.

(DR. RANCE *enters from the garden.*)

RANCE. I can find no trace of your secretary. I might add, Prentice, that my patience is all but exhausted. Unless I discover her whereabouts within the next few minutes you'll find yourself in serious trouble. (*Exits to the wards.*)

MRS. PRENTICE. (*Enters from the hall.*) They've called from the front desk. A policeman is in the hall. He wishes to speak to some member of the household.

PRENTICE. Ask him to wait. Tell him I'll see him in a moment.

(MRS. PRENTICE *goes into the hall.* NICK *stands and appeals to* DR. PRENTICE, *emotional.*)

NICK. Oh, sir! They've come to arrest me!

PRENTICE. This paranoia is uncalled for. The officer has probably called to ask me for the hand of my cook in marriage.

NICK. You're wrong, sir! They'll give me five years if I'm caught.

PRENTICE. Why are you in danger of arrest?

NICK. Well, sir, as your wife has already told you, I attempted last night to misbehave myself with her. I didn't succeed.

PRENTICE. I'm sure you didn't. Despite all appearances to the contrary, Mrs. Prentice is harder to get into than the reading room of the British Museum.

NICK. Undeterred I took the elevator to the third floor of the hotel where a party of schoolgirls were staying. Oh, sir, what lonely and aimless lives they lead! I did what I could to bring them some happiness.

PRENTICE. (*With a frown.*) Was there no mistress in attendance?

NICK. She occupied a room across the corridor.

PRENTICE. Did you disturb her?

NICK. No. And she'll never forgive me for it. It was she who reported the incident to the police. Oh, sir! Don't turn me over to the law.

(DR. RANCE *enters from the dispensary.*)

RANCE. I warn you, Prentice, unless you're prepared to cooperate in finding Miss Barclay I shall call upon you to account for her disappearance. If you're unable to do so the police must be informed. (*Goes into the garden.*)

PRENTICE. (*Turns to* NICK, *an idea dawning. Abruptly.*) Take your clothes off.

NICK. (*Pause.*) Are you going to fool around with me, sir?

PRENTICE. Certainly not! Is that what usually happens when men ask you to take your clothes off?

NICK. Yes. They usually give me money.

PRENTICE. How much? Oh, never mind. Strip! I want you to impersonate my secretary, Geraldine Barclay. It will solve both our problems. (*Gives* NICK *the dress.*) It's of particular importance to convince that man that you're my secretary. You should encounter no real difficulties there. He's an elderly man. I don't suppose he's checked with the original lately. That done, plead illness and leave the house. I'll be waiting with your own clothes. The operation completed, you'll be given a sum of money and a ticket for any destination you choose. If you run into trouble I shall deny all knowledge of you. Put this on. (*Hands* NICK *the dress.*)

(MRS. PRENTICE *enters from the hall. She stops in horror, seeing* NICK *only in his shorts.*)

MRS. PRENTICE. The policeman is still waiting. What devilry are you up to now?

PRENTICE. I'm carrying out a medical examination.

MRS. PRENTICE. But you're a psychiatrist. Why do you need the child undressed?

PRENTICE. (*Smiling, with enormous patience.*) My investigations upon his clothed body would be strictly "unscientific" and, inevitably, superficial. In order to assure myself that he's going to be of use to me I must examine him fully. And skin-wise.

MRS. PRENTICE. You ogre! Never, in my whole life, have I heard anything so lame and stupid. This folly will get you struck off the Medical Register. (*Picking up* NICK's *uniform.*) Come with me, dear. (*Takes the uniform into the garden.*)

NICK. What do we do now, sir? If that policeman comes in I can't even make a run for it.

PRENTICE. Dress in there. (*Shoves him toward the dis-

pensary. Then goes to the hall and calls in friendly tones.) Would you like to step this way, officer? I'm sorry to have kept you waiting.

NICK. Shoes, sir!

(DR. PRENTICE *swings round in alarm.)*

PRENTICE. Shoes! (*Takes* GERALDINE'S *shoe from* DR. RANCE'S *brief case and throws it to* NICK. *He goes to the vase and lifts the roses quickly. He puts a hand into the vase, searching for the other shoe.* SERGEANT MATCH *enters from the hall.* NICK *darts back into the dispensary.* DR. PRENTICE *holds the roses. In cold tones:*) Would you mind not entering my consulting room without permission?

MATCH. (*A little put out.*) You asked me to come in, sir.

PRENTICE. I don't believe I did. Wait outside.

(SERGEANT MATCH *leaves the room.* DR. PRENTICE *takes the roses and shakes* GERALDINE'S *shoe from the vase.* MRS. PRENTICE *enters from the garden.* PRENTICE, *caught with the flowers, hides the shoe behind his back and offers the roses to her. She steps back in amazement.*)

MRS. PRENTICE. What have you done with that boy? Why do you keep giving me flowers?

PRENTICE. It's because I'm very fond of you, my dear.

MRS. PRENTICE. Your actions grow wilder with every passing moment. Why were you rude to the policeman?

PRENTICE. He barged in without so much as a by-your-leave.

MRS. PRENTICE. But he said you asked him to come in. Had you forgotten?

PRENTICE. Yes. (*Pause.*) My memory isn't what it was. Tell him I'll see him now.

(MRS. PRENTICE *goes into the hall.*)

GERALDINE. Dr. Prentice. (*Enters from the dispensary. Her hair has been cut short. She is wearing the hospital nightdress.* NICK *enters just behind her; takes the shoe from* PRENTICE *and darts back into the dispensary.*)

PRENTICE. Miss Barclay! What are you doing here?

(SERGEANT MATCH *enters from the hall,* PRENTICE *shields* GERALDINE *from* MATCH *with his body.*)

MATCH. Sorry for the misunderstanding, sir.

PRENTICE. (*Turning, abrupt.*) Please remain outside. I think I made myself plain.

MATCH. (*Pause.*) You don't wish to see me?

PRENTICE. No.

GERALDINE. Nothing would induce me to remain on your staff a moment longer, Doctor. I wish to give notice.

PRENTICE. Your disclosures could ruin me. Give me a chance to get us out of this mess.

GERALDINE. You must put matters right by telling the truth.

PRENTICE. (*Pulls curtains round couch.*) Hide behind here. Nothing unpleasant will happen. You have my word as a gentleman.

GERALDINE. We must tell the truth!

PRENTICE. That's a thoroughly defeatist attitude. (*Bundles her behind the curtain.*)

GERALDINE. (*Looking through the curtain.*) At least give me back my clothes. I feel naked without them.

(DR. PRENTICE *offers the vase with the underwear in it.* GERALDINE *takes out underclothes and retreats behind curtains. As* PRENTICE *stands with roses in his hands and the vase,* MRS. PRENTICE *and* SERGEANT MATCH *enter from the hall.* MRS. PRENTICE *clutches* MATCH'S *arm.*)

MRS. PRENTICE. Oh, if he presents me with those flowers again I shall faint! (*They watch in silence as* DR.

PRENTICE *replaces the roses with an air of confidence. Without* GERALDINE'S *clothes under them the stalks are too short. The flowers vanish into the vase.* MRS. PRENTICE *cries out in surprise.*) Oh, he's cut the stalks off! His lunacy is beyond belief.

PRENTICE. Excuse my wife's hysteria. A man tried to molest her last night. Her recovery is far from complete.

MATCH. I understand that Mrs. Prentice introduced the young man to you, sir?

PRENTICE. Yes, but we won't prefer charges.

MATCH. I believe your wife to be ill-advised in not repeating her experiences before a judge and jury. However, as it happens, I'm not concerned with this case. I'm interested in the youth's movements between midnight and seven A.M. During that period he is alleged to have misconducted himself with a party of schoolchildren.

MRS. PRENTICE. How vile and disgraceful!

MATCH. Yes, ma'am. After carrying out a medical examination our lady doctor is up in arms. She can't wait to meet this fellow face to face.

PRENTICE. Well, Sergeant, he isn't on the premises. If he turns up you'll be informed.

MRS. PRENTICE. (*Shocked.*) How dare you give misleading information to the police? (*To* SERGEANT MATCH.) He was here. I have his clothes upstairs.

MATCH. Very wise of you to confiscate his clothing, ma'am. If more women did the same the number of cases of rape would be halved.

PRENTICE. (*At the desk.*) Or doubled.

MRS. PRENTICE. Disregard anything my husband says. I'll get the clothing. (*Goes into the garden.*)

MATCH. (*Turns to* DR. PRENTICE.) I'm also anxious, sir, to trace the whereabouts of a young woman called Barclay. (DR. PRENTICE *coughs.*) Can you help in my inquiries?

PRENTICE. Why do you wish to see Miss Barclay?

MATCH. It's a matter of national importance. Miss Barclay's—

PRENTICE. Shh! I must ask you to lower your voice. I specialize in patients who are allergic to sound. . . . They've been known to become violent at the merest whisper.

MATCH. Miss Barclay's stepmother, a woman of otherwise unblemished character, died recently. Shortly before her death her name had been linked in a most unpleasant way with that of Sir Winston Churchill. Mrs. Barclay's association with the great man gave offense in some circles. However, the local council, composed by and large of no-nonsense men and women in their sixties, decided in view of his war record to overlook Sir Winston's moral lapse. Under expert guidance he was to be reintegrated into society. The task accomplished, it became clear that the great man was incomplete. The council decided to sue the heirs of Mrs. Barclay for those parts of Sir Winston which an army-type medical had proved to be missing. The council's lawyers obtained an exhumation order. Early this morning Mrs. Barclay's coffin was opened in the presence of the Lord Mayor and Lady Mayoress of this borough. Fainting women were held back as the official in charge searched high and low for council property. His efforts were not crowned with success. Mrs. Barclay had taken nothing with her to the grave except those things which she ought to have done. That is when the matter came to the attention of the police.

PRENTICE. You suspect my secretary of having stolen certain parts of Sir Winston Churchill?

MATCH. Yes.

(MRS. PRENTICE *enters, with* NICK'S *uniform, from the garden.*)

MRS. PRENTICE. Sergeant, here is proof that the young man was in this room.

MATCH. He can't get far without clothing.

PRENTICE. His progress without clothing last night was enviable.

MATCH. (*To* DR. PRENTICE.) You still claim, sir, that you have no knowledge of the youth's whereabouts?

PRENTICE. Yes.

MATCH. And what has become of Miss Barclay?

PRENTICE. I've no idea.

MRS. PRENTICE. You told Dr. Rance she was burning the tarbabies. (SERGEANT MATCH *looks from one to the other in amazement.*) Was that a lie?

PRENTICE. It may have been. I can't remember.

MRS. PRENTICE. (*Gives an impatient toss of her head.*) You must talk to Dr. Rance, Sergeant. He's from the government. He may be able to account for my husband's unusual behavior pattern. Please tell him that his specialized knowledge is urgently required.

MATCH. Where would the doctor be?

MRS. PRENTICE. In the garden. (SERGEANT MATCH *goes into the garden.*) Now, darling, try to remember why you damaged the flowers in this vase. It may have a direct bearing on the case. (*Exits to the garden with the vase.*)

GERALDINE. (*Pokes her head through the curtain.*) Tell the truth, sir. All your troubles spring from a lack of candor.

PRENTICE. My troubles spring from a misguided attempt to seduce you.

GERALDINE. (*With a gasp.*) You never told me you were seducing me. You said you were interested in my mind.

(SERGEANT MATCH *appears from the garden.* GERALDINE *ducks behind the curtain.*)

MATCH. Are you sure that Dr. Rance is out here, sir?

PRENTICE. Yes.

MATCH. Where would he be then?

PRENTICE. In the shrubbery. We've a naked elf on a birdbath. We often have trouble with Peeping Toms.

MATCH. I'd like you to accompany me, sir.

(DR. PRENTICE *shrugs and follows* SERGEANT MATCH *into the garden.* GERALDINE *steps down from the couch. She is wearing her panties and bra. She carries the nightgown. She picks up* NICK'S *uniform. She hurries to the dispensary. She retreats at once dropping the nightgown. She scurries to the hall, checks herself and scuttles back to the couch. She climbs behind the curtains. As* NICK *enters from the dispensary, dressed in women's clothing,* MRS. PRENTICE *enters from the garden with the roses in a small vase.*)

MRS. PRENTICE. Are you Geraldine Barclay?

NICK. Yes.

MRS. PRENTICE. Where have you been?

NICK. (*Primly.*) I've been attending to the thousand and one duties that occupy the average secretary during her working hours.

MRS. PRENTICE. It doesn't take the whole morning to file your nails, surely?

NICK. I had to lie down. I was sick.

MRS. PRENTICE. Are you pregnant?

NICK. I can't discuss my employer's business with you.

MRS. PRENTICE. What was your last job?

NICK. I was a hostess at the "One, Two, Three" Club.

MRS. PRENTICE. (*Purses her lips in disapproval.*) It's obvious that you're unsuited to the work here. I shan't recommend you for employment. (DR. PRENTICE *and* SERGEANT MATCH *enter from the garden. To* SERGEANT MATCH.) Ah, Sergeant. This is Geraldine Barclay. She'll be happy to help you in your inquiries.

MATCH. (*To* NICK.) Miss Barclay, I must ask you to produce, or cause to be produced, the missing parts of Sir Winston Churchill.

NICK. What do they look like?

MATCH. You're claiming ignorance of the shape and structure of the objects sought?

NICK. I'm in the dark.

MATCH. You handled them only at night? We shall draw our own concusions.

NICK. I'm not the sort of girl to be mixed up in that kind of thing. I'm an ex-member of the Brownies.

MATCH. Are you concealing unlawful property about your person?

NICK. No.

MATCH. I'll have to call medical evidence to prove your story, miss. You must be thoroughly looked into.

PRENTICE. I'm a qualified doctor.

MATCH. Only women are permitted to examine female suspects.

PRENTICE. Doesn't that breed discontent in the force?

MATCH. Among the single men there's a certain amount of bitterness. Married men who are familiar with the country are glad to be let off extra map-reading.

MRS. PRENTICE. Sergeant, I'll examine Miss Barclay. That will solve all our problems. Come along, Miss Barclay.

MATCH. Thank you, ma'am. I accept your kind offer.

(MRS. PRENTICE *leads* NICK *into the garden. A siren sounds from the wards; then a buzzer.* DR. RANCE *enters from the wards.*)

RANCE. Prentice! The patient has escaped. I've sounded the alarm.

MATCH. How long has the patient been gone, sir?

RANCE. Only a few minutes. This is her gown. She must be naked then.

MATCH. Any steps you feel may be necessary to recover your patient may be taken, sir. (DR. RANCE *crosses, hurries into the hall.*) She must've come through this room. You and I were in the garden. Mrs. Prentice was upstairs. Escape would be out of the question. She must still be in this room. (*Turns to* DR. PRENTICE *in triumph.*) Only one hiding place is possible. (*Pulls the curtain on the couch aside.* GERALDINE *is revealed. She is wearing*

NICK'S *uniform, his hat. Taking in the picture at a glance.*) Are you from the Station Hotel?

GERALDINE. (*Answers in a scared voice.*) Yes.

MATCH. I want a word with you, my lad. (*Takes out his notebook. The siren and buzzer wail.*)

BLACKOUT

CURTAIN

ACT TWO

Continuous. The siren and buzzer. They stop. EVERYONE *is as they were at the end of ACT ONE.*

MATCH. Are you from the Station Hotel?

GERALDLNE. Yes.

MATCH. I want a word with you, my lad. You're under arrest.

GERALDINE. (*To* SERGEANT MATCH.) You've no idea how glad I am to be arrested.

MATCH. Why?

GERALDINE. I'm in great danger.

MATCH. Who from?

GERALDINE. Dr. Prentice. His conduct is scandalous. Take me to the police station. I shall prefer charges.

MATCH. (*To* DR. PRENTICE.) Have you anything to say, sir?

PRENTICE. Yes. What this young woman claims is a tissue of lies.

MATCH. (*Pause.*) This is a boy, sir. Not a girl. If you're baffled by the difference it might be as well to approach both with caution. (*To* GERALDINE.) Let's hear what you've got to say for yourself.

GERALDINE. I came here for a job. On some pretext the doctor got me to remove my clothes. Afterwards he behaved in a strange manner.

MATCH. (*Glances at* DR. PRENTICE *in disapproval.* MATCH *turns to* GERALDINE. *Quietly.*) Did he, at any time, attempt to interfere with you?

PRENTICE. You'll be disappointed, Sergeant, if you imagine that that boy has lost his virginity.

MATCH. I hope he'll be considerably more experienced before he loses that, sir. What reason had you for taking off his clothes?

PRENTICE. I wished to assure myself of his unquestioning obedience. I give a prize each year.

MATCH. Have you been in trouble of this kind before?

PRENTICE. I'm not in trouble.

MATCH. You must realize this boy is bringing a serious charge against you?

PRENTICE. Yes. It's ridiculous. I'm a married man.

MATCH. Marriage excuses no one the freak's roll-call.

PRENTICE. I'm a respected member of my profession. Your accusations are absurd.

MATCH. It's not for me to bring accusations in a matter I don't fully understand.

PRENTICE. The boy has an unsavory reputation. Last night requires explanining before this morning.

GERALDINE. I had nothing to do with the disgraceful happenings at the Station Hotel.

MATCH. You deny that on the night of Thursday last you did behave in an obscene manner with a section of the Priory Road School for Girls?

GERALDINE. Yes.

MATCH. Nicholas Becket, I warn you that anything you say will be taken down and may be used in evidence against you.

GERALDINE. My name is not Nicholas Beckett.

MATCH. (*Pause, with a frown.*) Then why d'you suppose I'd wish to arrest you?

GERALDINE. To safeguard my interests?

PRENTICE. You imagine you'll be safe from acts of indecency in a police station?

GERALDINE. Of course.

PRENTICE. I wish I shared your optimism.

RANCE. (*Enters from the hall.*) Full security arrangements are in force. No one is to leave the clinic without written permission. Prentice, get your secretary to issue warrants to every member of the staff.

PRENTICE. I'll do that, sir, as soon as she's ready to resume her normal duties.

MATCH. Are you Dr. Rance?

RANCE. Yes.

MATCH. (*To* DR. RANCE.) Would you help us clear up a spot of trouble, Doctor? It's a matter of some urgency. Last night this young man assaulted a number of female schoolchildren. This morning he was assaulted in his turn.

RANCE. (*With a shrug.*) What can I say? It's a case of "be done by as you did."

MATCH. The boy has made a serious charge against Dr. Prentice. He claims he was forced to strip and lie on a couch.

RANCE. (*To* DR. PRENTICE.) A complete list of your indiscretions would make a best seller. Have you behaved in an unseemly manner?

PRENTICE. No! It's just that my nerves are on edge.

RANCE. You should consult a qualified psychiatrist.

PRENTICE. I am a qualified psychiatrist.

RANCE. You're a fool. That isn't quite the same thing. Though, in your case, the two may have much in common. (*To* SERGEANT MATCH.) Has the boy come to your notice before?

MATCH. Not on a case of this kind. That's why we have to be careful. As the doctor rightly says, he has an unsavory reputation. It may be that he bears Dr. Prentice a grudge.

RANCE. (*To* DR. PRENTICE.) Perhaps this accusation springs from disappointment. It might have been wiser if you hadn't rejected the young fellow's blandishments.

PRENTICE. Unnatural vice can ruin a man.

RANCE. Ruin follows the accusation, not the vice. Had you committed the act you wouldn't now be facing the charge.

PRENTICE. I couldn't commit the act. I'm a heterosexual.

RANCE. I wish you wouldn't use these Chaucerian words. It's most confusing. (*To* SERGEANT MATCH.) How do you propose to get to the bottom of this affair?

MATCH. A reputable person must examine the lad.

GERALDINE. I refuse to be examined!

MATCH. You can't refuse. You're under arrest.

GERALDINE. I'm not Nicholas Beckett. I want to be taken to prison.

MATCH. If you aren't Nicholas Beckett you can't go to prison. You're not under arrest.

GERALDINE. (*Pause, biting her lip.*) I am Nicholas Beckett.

MATCH. Then you're under arrest. You'll submit to a medical examination.

RANCE. And I shall conduct it. The mind of the victim of this kind of assault must be considered equally with the body.

GERALDINE. I haven't been assaulted.

RANCE. Then why make such a foul accusation?

GERALDINE. I didn't accuse anyone. The sergeant made the accusation.

RANCE. (*To* SERGEANT MATCH.) Has Dr. Prentice assaulted you too? (*To* DR. PRENTICE.) Is it policemen or young boys you're after? At your age it's high time you came to a decision. (*To* SERGEANT MATCH.) Wait outside. I shall examine the boy and make my report. Afterwards I'll take a look at you, too.

MATCH. (*Stunned.*) At me?

RANCE. Yes. We can't be too careful.

MATCH. It seems a bit unusual, sir.

RANCE. You're in a madhouse. Unusual behavior is the order of the day.

MATCH. Only for patients.

RANCE. We've no privileged class here. We practice democratic lunacy. (SERGEANT MATCH *goes into the hall.*) Take your clothes off, sonny. Lie on the couch.

GERALDINE. I shouldn't've behaved as I did, sir. I wasn't harmed.

RANCE. You enjoyed the experience? Would you enjoy normal intercourse?

GERALDINE. No. I might get pregnant— (*Realizes her mistake and attempts to cover up.*) —or be the cause of pregnancy in others.

RANCE. (*Quick to notice the error, turns to* DR. PRENTICE.) He's just given away a vital piece of information. (*Advances on* GERALDINE.) Do you think of yourself as a girl?

GERALDINE. No.

RANCE. Why not?

GERALDINE. I'm a boy.

RANCE. (*Kindly.*) Do you have the evidence about you?

GERALDINE. (*Her eyes flashing an appeal to* DR. PRENTICE.) I must be a boy. I like girls.

RANCE. (*Stops and wrinkles his brow, puzzled. Aside, to* DR. PRENTICE.) I can't quite follow the reasoning there.

PRENTICE. Many men imagine that a preference for women is, ipso facto, a proof of virility.

RANCE. (*Nodding, sagely.*) Someone should really write a book on these folk myths. (*To* GERALDINE.) Take your trousers down. I'll tell you which sex you belong to.

GERALDINE. (*Backing away.*) I'd rather not know!

RANCE. You wish to remain in ignorance?

GERALDINE. Yes.

RANCE. I can't encourage you in such a self-indulgent attitude. You must face facts like the rest of us. (*Forces* GERALDINE *back to the couch.*)

PRENTICE. You're forcing the boy to undergo a repetition of a traumatic experience, sir. He might go insane.

RANCE. This is a mental home. He couldn't choose a more appropriate place. (*To* GERALDINE.) Undress. My time is valuable.

GERALDINE. (*Unable to stand the ordeal any longer, cries out to* DR. PRENTICE *in anguish.*) I can't go on, Doctor! I must tell the truth. (*To* DR. RANCE.) I'm not a boy! I'm a girl!

RANCE. (*To* DR. PRENTICE.) Excellent. A confession at last. He wishes to believe he's a girl in order to minimize the feelings of guilt after homosexual intercourse.

GERALDINE. (*Wild-eye, desperate.*) I pretended to be a boy. I did it to help Dr. Prentice.

RANCE. How does it help a man if a girl pretends to be a boy?

GERALDINE. Wives are angry if they find their husbands have undressed and seduced a girl.

RANCE. But boys are fair game? I doubt whether your very personal view of society would go unchallenged.

(*Provoked beyond endurance,* GERALDINE *flings herself into* DR. RANCE'S *arms and cries hysterically.*)

GERALDINE. Undress me then, Doctor! Do whatever you like, only prove that I'm a girl.

RANCE. (*Pushes away and turns, frigidly, to* DR. PRENTICE.) If he's going to carry on like this he'll have to be strapped down.

(MRS. PRENTICE *enters from the garden.*)

MRS. PRENTICE. (*To* DR. RANCE.) Dr. Rance, would you take a look at Miss Barclay? She refuses to undress in front of a woman.

RANCE. How about in front of a man?

MRS. PRENTICE. I haven't sounded her on the subject.

RANCE. I wonder if I could tempt her. I'll give it a try. She may be a nymphomaniac. (*To* DR. PRENTICE.) If this boy becomes foul-mouthed keep him on the boil till I return. (*Goes to the garden, followed by* MRS. PRENTICE. GERALDINE *pulls herself together.*)

GERALDINE. I'll go through the garden, Doctor. I can get a taxi home.

PRENTICE. That isn't possible. Dr. Rance has arranged for strict security precautions to be in force until the patient is recaptured.

GERALDINE. When the patient is recaptured can I go?

PRENTICE. No.

GERALDINE. Why not?

PRENTICE. You *are* the patient.

(GERALDINE *gives a little cry of distress.* DR. RANCE *re-enters.*)

RANCE. Prentice, your secretary is standing on a table fighting off any attempt to undress her. She seems incapable of conducting herself in a proper manner.

PRENTICE. She's given me no cause for complaint.

RANCE. But you expect a secretary to misbehave herself. It's a condition of employment. (*Faces* DR. PRENTICE, *candidly.*) Do you realize the woman uses a razor?

PRENTICE. I see nothing remarkable in that. Mrs. Prentice has occasion sometimes to remove unwanted hair.

RANCE. From her chin? There are two sexes. The unpalatable truth must be faced. Your attempts at a merger can end in heartbreak.

(MRS. PRENTICE *enters from the garden, a syringe in her hand, leading a chastened* NICK *by the hand.*)

MRS. PRENTICE. Miss Barclay is calmer now, Doctor. I've given her a sedative.

RANCE. (*Turning to* NICK, *shaking his head.*) What an absorbing picture of the mind in decay. Why won't you allow Mrs. Prentice to undress you?

MRS. PRENTICE. Her objections appear to be religious. She claims to be at one with God.

RANCE. Come here, sonny. Were you present when Dr. Prentice used this youth unnaturally?

NICK. What is unnatural?

RANCE. (*To* MRS. PRENTICE.) How disturbing the questions of the mad can be.

MRS. PRENTICE. (*Nodding to* GERALDINE.) Has my husband misbehaved with that boy?

RANCE. It's impossible to say with any degree of accuracy. He refuses to cooperate with a medical examination.

MRS. PRENTICE. (*To* DR. PRENTICE.) What happened to the other boy?

RANCE. Which boy?

MRS. PRENTICE. The one my husband undressed.

RANCE. This is the boy he undressed.

MRS. PRENTICE. No. He undressed the boy who made a nuisance of himself to me.

RANCE. (*Pause.*) Isn't this the same one?

MRS. PRENTICE. No.

RANCE. (*Staring, perplexed.*) There's another boy?

MRS. PRENTICE. He was being interviewed for a secretarial post. My husband made him undress.

RANCE. (*Coldly, to* DR. PRENTICE.) How long have you been a pervert?

PRENTICE. I'm not a pervert!

RANCE. How would you describe a man who mauls young boys, importunes policemen and lives on terms of intimacy with a woman who shaves twice a day?

PRENTICE. I'd say the man was a pervert.

RANCE. I'm glad you're beginning to face the realities of the situation. (*To* GERALDINE.) Who are you if you're not Nicholas Beckett?

(GERALDINE *looks to* DR. PRENTICE *and bites her lip.*)

PRENTICE. His name is Gerald Barclay.

RANCE. (*Indicating* NICK.) Is he this young woman's brother?

PRENTICE. No.

RANCE. What happened then to Nicholas Beckett?

PRENTICE. He left an hour ago to resume his duties at the Station Hotel.

MRS. PRENTICE. He can't have! I took his uniform. He'd be naked.

PRENTICE. From what one hears of the Station Hotel the uniform is optional.

RANCE. (*Shaking his head, worried.*) I hope we haven't lost another one. We'll be alone with our miracle drugs if many more go. (*To* MRS. PRENTICE.) Find out whether the boy has returned to the hotel.

MRS. PRENTICE. I'll call immediately. (*Goes into the hall.*)

RANCE. (*Turns to* DR. PRENTICE.) Prepare the necessary papers. I'm certifying these two.

(*Cries of alarm come from* NICK *and* GERALDINE.)

NICK. Can't you do something about him, sir? He's off his head.

RANCE. (*Sternly.*) I am a representative of order, you of chaos. Unless that fact is faced, I can never hope to cure you. (*To* DR. PRENTICE.) Make out the committal orders for me to sign.

PRENTICE. (*Upset and angry.*) I can't agree to such drastic action. We've no evidence of insanity. These children are no more ill than I am.

RANCE. But your condition is worse than hers.

PRENTICE. I can't accept that.

RANCE. No madman ever accepts madness. Only the sane do that. I'm relieving you of your post as head of the clinic. You'll do as I say from now on.

PRENTICE. I resent your handling of this affair, sir. I shall make my views known to the commissioners.

RANCE. I doubt whether the views of a madman will carry much weight with the commissioners.

PRENTICE. I'm not mad. It only looks that way.

RANCE. Your actions today could get the Archbishop of Canterbury declared non-compos.

PRENTICE. I'm not the Archbishop of Canterbury.

RANCE. That will come at a later stage of your illness.

PRENTICE. Your interpretation of my behavior is misplaced and erroneous. If anyone borders on lunacy it's you yourself!

RANCE. Bearing in mind your abnormality, that is a normal reaction. The sane appear as strange to the mad as the mad to the sane. Take two of these. (*Takes red pillbox from pocket.*)

PRENTICE. (*Looking at the pillbox.*) What are they?

RANCE. Dangerous drugs intended to relieve your pathologically elevated mood. Be careful not to exceed the stated dose. I shall return shortly. All of you remain here. (*Exits to the wards.*)

NICK. Why is he wearing my uniform?

GERALDINE. Why is she wearing my shoes?

PRENTICE. He isn't a boy. He's a girl. She isn't a girl. She's a boy. And we'll all be sharing the same cell at this rate.

NICK. If we changed clothes, sir, we could get things back to normal.

PRENTICE. We'd then have to account for the disappearance of my secretary and the page boy.

GERALDINE. But they don't exist!

PRENTICE. When people who don't exist disappear the account of their departure must be convincing.

NICK. (*Pause.*) Is the policeman corruptible?

PRENTICE. Why?

NICK. I must have his uniform.

PRENTICE. For what reason?

NICK. To arrest Nicholas Beckett.

PRENTICE. But you're Nicholas Beckett.

NICK. Once I've arrested myself you can write me off.

GERALDINE. Aren't you multiplying our problems instead of dividing them?

NICK. (*To* DR. PRENTICE.) Some glib pretext will get her out of the way. Then she and I can change clothes.

(DR. RANCE *enters from the wards.*)

RANCE. I'm putting this youth into a padded cell. Rampant hermaphroditism must be discouraged.

PRENTICE. Quite right.

GERALDINE. (*With a sob.*) Twice declared insane in one day! And they said I'd be working for a cheerful, well-spoken crowd. Oh, I'm glad my parents are dead. This would've killed them. (DR. RANCE *takes her to the wards.*)

PRENTICE. (*To* NICK.) I'll get the sergeant to undress so you can have his uniform. I'm suspected of the offense, I might as well commit it. We'll need something to calm him down. A mild tranquilizer wouldn't harm him, I suppose. You'll find a box of anti-depressants in the top right-hand drawer of my desk. (NICK *goes to the desk and takes a square, white pillbox from the drawer.* DR. PRENTICE *opens the hall door. Calling, friendly.*) Would you step this way, Sergeant? (*To* NICK.) Hide in there.

(NICK *hands* DR. PRENTICE *the white pillbox and hides in the closet.* SERGEANT MATCH *enters from the hall.*)

MATCH. You wish to speak to me, Doctor?

PRENTICE. Yes. Dr. Rance has asked me to examine you. I'd like you to undress and lie on that couch.

MATCH. (*Pause.*) I haven't been interfered with.

PRENTICE. Never mind about that. Strip down to your underwear.

MATCH. (*Sitting on couch, unlacing boots.*) If you make any attempt to arouse me, Doctor, I shall call for help.

PRENTICE. It's easy to see why you've never been interfered with. You place too many obstacles in the way. Come along. Come along. Speed is essential.

(SERGEANT MATCH *takes off his boots.* NICK *appears from the closet.* DR. PRENTICE *hands him the boots.* SERGEANT MATCH *takes off his tunic and hands it to* DR. PRENTICE. DR. PRENTICE *throws tunic to* NICK *who retreats.* SERGEANT MATCH *drops his trousers.* MRS. PRENTICE *enters from the hall. Seeing the* SERGEANT *without his trousers, she screams loudly. Shocked and embarrassed,* SERGEANT MATCH *pulls up his trousers.*)

MRS. PRENTICE. (*Icily.*) What were you doing with your trousers down, officer?

MATCH. The doctor is going to examine me.

MRS. PRENTICE. Why?

MATCH. There's reason to suppose that I had a nasty experience a short time ago.

MRS. PRENTICE. What kind of experience?

PRENTICE. He was meddled with.

MRS. PRENTICE. By whom?

PRENTICE. Me.

MRS. PRENTICE. And why are you examining him?

PRENTICE. To find out whether his story is true.

MRS. PRENTICE. Don't you know?

PRENTICE. No. I didn't feel a thing.

MRS. PRENTICE. (*With a toss of her head.*) Where is Dr. Rance?

PRENTICE. He's just certified the hotel page. He's putting him in a padded cell.

MRS. PRENTICE. I must speak to him. Things are getting out of control. (*Hurries into the ward.*)

PRENTICE. (*Turns to* SERGEANT MATCH.) Remove your trousers, Sergeant, and we'll continue. (SERGEANT MATCH *takes off his trousers and hands them to* DR. PRENTICE. *He is naked except for his underpants and socks. With a flourish* DR. PRENTICE *takes the red pillbox from his pocket and hands it to the* SERGEANT. *Smiling.*) Swallow these. Take as many as you like. They're quite harmless. (*The* SERGEANT *accepts the box.*) Now I want you to lie on this couch and concentrate on the closing chapters of your favorite work of fiction. (SERGEANT MATCH *lies on the couch.* DR. PRENTICE *pulls the curtain around him and hurries to the closet with the trousers. He meets* NICK *in the doorway.* NICK *carries the* SERGEANT'S *uniform.* DR. PRENTICE *hands him the trousers. To* NICK.) In the garden you'll find a little summerhouse. You won't be disturbed in there. (NICK *goes into the garden with the clothes.* DR. PRENTICE *goes to the desk.* NICK *reappears, without the uniform.*)

NICK. The helmet, sir!

PRENTICE. (*Hurries to the couch.*) The helmet, Sergeant!

MATCH. (*From behind the curtain.*) In the hall, sir.

PRENTICE. (*To* NICK.) Miss Barclay's clothes are in the closet.

(NICK *hurries into the hall, with the uniform to get the helmet.* MRS. PRENTICE *enters from the ward.* NICK *re-enters from the hall, wearing only underpants and the helmet. Upon seeing him,* MRS. PRENTICE *shrieks and follows* NICK *into the garden.* DR. PRENTICE *ducks under the desk and runs into the hall with the dress [the one* NICK *has just changed out of] and* GERALDINE'S *shoes [which* NICK *has also just left there].*)

MRS. PRENTICE. (*Re-enters alone.*) This place is like a madhouse!

RANCE. (*Enters from the wards.*) Where is Dr. Prentice?

MRS. PRENTICE. I don't know. When I returned from telephoning the Station Hotel he was undressing the sergeant.

RANCE. How would you describe his relations with the sergeant?

MRS. PRENTICE. Strange and, in many ways, puzzling. He's called him into this room on several occasions and then abruptly dismissed him.

RANCE. Playing the coquette, eh? Well, well, it adds spice to a love affair. What news of the missing patient?

MRS. PRENTICE. None.

RANCE. And what's the report from the Station Hotel?

MRS. PRENTICE. They state that they have no page called Gerald Barclay on their register. The youth you've certified insane must be an impostor.

RANCE. And what of Nicholas Beckett—the real page boy?

MRS. PRENTICE. He hasn't returned to the hotel. And when he disappeared his uniform was in my possession.

RANCE. (*Greatly concerned.*) Two young people—one mad and one sexually insatiable—both naked—are roaming this house. At all costs we must prevent a collision. Oh, this is incredible. When I publish it, I'll make my fortune. My "documentary type" novelette will go into twelve record-breaking reprints. I'll be able to leave the service of the government and bask in the attentions of those who, like myself, find other people's iniquity puts money in their purse. (DR. RANCE *picks up red pillbox from floor in front of couch.*) What's this? The pills I gave your husband? It's empty. He's taken an overdose! We have here terrible evidence of conflict. His tormented mind, seeking release, has led him to attempt to destroy himself.

MRS. PRENTICE. (*Gasps with shock and amazement.*) Suicide? This is so unexpected.

RANCE. Just when one least expects it, the unexpected always happens. We must find him before it's too late.

(*They both exit into the hall.* DR. PRENTICE *and* NICK *enter simultaneously from the dispensary and the garden.* DR. PRENTICE *carries the shoes and dress.* NICK *is wearing the* SERGEANT'S *uniform.*)

PRENTICE. Miss Barclay has escaped from the padded cell! (*A sound from behind the curtains. They part the curtains of the couch and* SERGEANT MATCH *tumbles forward drugged into insensibility.* DR. PRENTICE *and* NICK *react to the* SERGEANT'S *condition and catch him. They place him in a sitting position in a chair.* DR. PRENTICE *feels in his pocket and pulls out the square white pillbox. His eyes widen. He clutches his throat.*) My God! I've poisoned him! (DR. PRENTICE *puts the dress down and attempts to drag* SERGEANT MATCH *to his feet. The* SERGEANT *moans, stares about him in a stupor and shivers uncontrollably.*)

NICK. (*Holding the* SERGEANT'S *pulse.*) He's frozen, sir.

PRENTICE. The effect of the drug. We find the same process at work in corpses. He'll be all right if we get him in the open air so he can sleep it off.

NICK. Get some clothes on him and dump him outside. (*He picks up the dress.*)

PRENTICE. (*Wringing his hands.*) How will I explain the presence in my garden of the drugged police sergeant?

NICK. (*Putting the dress onto* SERGEANT MATCH.) You're guilty. You don't have to explain. Only the innocent do that.

PRENTICE. (*Puts* GERALDINE'S *shoes in his pants pockets. He and* NICK *carry* SERGEANT MATCH *to the garden in the chair.*) Oh, if this ever gets out I'll be reduced to casting horoscopes.

(MRS. PRENTICE *enters from the hall, followed immediately by* DR. RANCE. *They look at each other for an instant. She exits to the garden,* RANCE *to the wards. They both re-enter immediately.*)

MRS. PRENTICE. Dr. Rance, I've just seen my husband carrying a woman into the shrubbery.

RANCE. Was she struggling?

MRS. PRENTICE. No.

RANCE. Then a new and frightening possibility presents itself. The drugs in this box— (*He lifts up the bright red pillbox.*) —may not have been used for suicide, but for murder. Your husband has made away with his secretary!

MRS. PRENTICE. Isn't that a little melodramatic, Doctor?

RANCE. Lunatics *are* melodramatic. The subtleties of drama are wasted on them. Everything is now clear. The final chapters of my book are knitting together: incest, buggery, outrageous women and strange love-cults catering to depraved appetites. All the fashionable bric-a-brac. (*To* MRS. PRENTICE.) My "unbiased account" of the case of the infamous sex-killer Prentice will undoubtedly add a great deal to our understanding of such creatures. Society must be made aware of the growing menace of pornography. The whole treacherous avant-garde movement will be exposed for what it is—an instrument for inciting decent citizens to commit bizarre crimes against humanity and the state! (*He pauses, a little overcome, and wipes his brow.*) You have, under your roof, my dear, one of the most remarkable lunatics of all time. We must institute a search for the corpse. As a transvestite, fetishist, bisexual murderer Dr. Prentice displays considerable deviation overlap. We may get necrophilia too. As a sort of bonus. (DR. PRENTICE *enters from the garden with an empty chair; replaces it by the desk. He still has the shoes in his pockets. Turning, and giving a disdainful stare:*) Would you confirm, Prentice, that your wife saw you carrying a body into the shrubbery?

PRENTICE. Yes. I have an explanation for my conduct.

RANCE. I'm not interested in your explanations. I can provide my own. Where is your secretary?

PRENTICE. I've given her the sack. (*Puts shoes on the desk.*)

RANCE. (*Aside to* MRS. PRENTICE.) He killed her and wrapped her body in a sack. The word association is very clear.

PRENTICE. I haven't killed anyone!

RANCE. Your answer is in accord with the complex structure of your neurosis.

PRENTICE. The person my wife saw wasn't dead. They were asleep.

RANCE. (*To* MRS. PRENTICE.) He hopes for a resurrection. We've a link here with primitive religion. (*To* DR. PRENTICE.) Why have you turned your back on the God of your fathers?

PRENTICE. I'm a rationalist.

RANCE. You can't be a rationalist in an irrational world. It isn't rational. (*Pointing to the shoes.*) Was it your intention to wear these shoes for auto-erotic excitement?

PRENTICE. No, I'm a perfectly normal man.

RANCE. (*To* MRS. PRENTICE.) His belief in normality is quite abnormal. (*To* DR. PRENTICE.) Was the girl killed before or after you took her clothes off?

PRENTICE. He wasn't a girl. He was a man.

MRS. PRENTICE. He was wearing a dress.

PRENTICE. He was a man for all that.

RANCE. Women wear dresses, Prentice, not men. I won't be a party to the wanton destruction of a fine old tradition. Did you change clothes with your victim before it died?

PRENTICE. Nobody died! The person you saw me with was a policeman who'd taken an overdose of narcotics.

MRS. PRENTICE. Why was he dressed as a woman?

PRENTICE. He was naked when I found him. The dress was readily to hand.

MRS. PRENTICE. Where were his own clothes?

PRENTICE. A boy had stolen them. (DR. RANCE *draws* MRS. PRENTICE *aside, his face a mask of disapproval.*)

RANCE. Mrs. Prentice, the time has come to call a halt to this Graeco-Roman hallucination. Is there a strait jacket in the house?

MRS. PRENTICE. Modern methods of treatment have rendered the strait jacket obsolete.

RANCE. I'm well aware of that. We still use them nonetheless. Have you one here?

MRS. PRENTICE. The porter has a few.

RANCE. We can take no chances with your husband in his present condition. Keep him occupied until I return. (*He goes.*)

PRENTICE. Is this another of your plots to undermine my reputation for sound judgment, you treacherous harpy?

MRS. PRENTICE. (*Gently.*) Dr. Rance believes that you've caused a poor girl's death, darling. You may be called upon to accept a period of restraint.

PRENTICE. Miss Barclay isn't dead!

MRS. PRENTICE. Produce her then and your difficulties will be over.

PRENTICE. I can't.

MRS. PRENTICE. Why not?

PRENTICE. You're wearing her dress. (*With a shrug of resignation.*) You surprised me this morning when I was attempting to seduce her.

MRS. PRENTICE. (*Smiles a smile of disbelief.*) If we're to save our marriage, my dear, you must admit that you prefer boys to women.

PRENTICE. (*Is stunned by her suggestion. He rounds on her in a fury.*) I won't have you making scandalous allegations about a matter of which you know nothing.

MRS. PRENTICE. (*Tossing her head.*) The page at the hotel accused you of behaving in an indecent manner.

PRENTICE. That wasn't a boy. It was a girl.

MRS. PRENTICE. Admit that you prefer your sex to mine. I've no hesitation in saying that I do.

PRENTICE. You filthy degenerate! Take your clothes off! (*He unzips her dress.*)

MRS. PRENTICE. (*Eagerly.*) Are you going to beat me? Do if you wish. Your psychotic experiences are immensely valuable to you and should be encouraged rather than thwarted or repressed. (*Gasping as he slaps her.*) Oh, my darling! This is the way to sexual adjustment in marriage. (RANCE *enters from the hall with two strait jackets, a witness to the final moment.* PRENTICE *picks up the dress, throws it over his arm; and with the shoes he exits proudly into the garden.*)

RANCE. What are you doing?

MRS. PRENTICE. Oh, Doctor, during your absence my husband became violent and struck me.

RANCE. Did you enjoy it?

MRS. PRENTICE. At first. But the pleasures of the senses quickly pall.

RANCE. We must lose no time in putting Dr. Prentice under restraint. We'll need help in the enterprise. Have you no brawny youth upon whom you can call in time of stress?

MRS. PRENTICE. I'm a married woman, Doctor! Your suggestion is in the worst of taste.

(NICK *enters from the garden dressed in the* SERGEANT'S *uniform.*)

NICK. Doctor, I'd like a word with you about my brother, Nicholas Beckett. I've just arrested him.

RANCE. Why?

NICK. He'd broken the law.

RANCE. And because of that he's to be treated as a common criminal? What's happened to the Anglo-Saxon love of fair play? Did you see Dr. Prentice in the garden?

NICK. No.

RANCE. We must find him. We have reason to believe he has killed his secretary.

NICK. (*Horrified.*) He can't have. He's got the Order of the Garter.

RANCE. These cabalistic signs are of no more use in warding off evil than the moons and stars on a sorcerer's hat. We shall need your help in tracking down that mindless killer.

NICK. (*With a groan.*) Oh, Doctor, I'm sick of all this. I have to make a confession.

RANCE. You must call for an appointment. I can't listen to confessions off the cuff.

NICK. I am Nicholas Beckett. (*Takes off his helmet.*) I dressed as Geraldine Barclay at the doctor's request, never imagining that I was unwittingly assisting a psychopath. (*To* MRS. PRENTICE.) That's why I objected to being undressed. It would've embarrassed me.

RANCE. Have you aided other men in their perverted follies?

NICK. During my last term at school I was the slave of a corporal in the Army.

RANCE. Were you never warned of the dangers inherent in such relationships?

NICK. When he was sent overseas he left me a copy of "The Way to Healthy Manhood."

RANCE. (*Drily, to* MRS. PRENTICE.) A case of opening the barn door after the horse is in. (*To* NICK. *He picks up the strait jacket.*) This is a strait jacket. I require your help in persuading Dr. Prentice to put it on. There may be violence. His body has a mind of its own. (*To* MRS. PRENTICE.) Have you any guns?

MRS. PRENTICE. Guns?

RANCE. (*Opens a drawer in the desk and takes out two guns.*) Oh, here. There are two. Take one.

MRS. PRENTICE. You will make sure before you fire that my husband isn't waving an olive branch?

RANCE. An olive branch can be used as an offensive weapon. I'm loath to certify a fellow psychiatrist. It causes such bad feelings within the profession. (*Goes into the garden.*)

MRS. PRENTICE. (*To* NICK.) Take no chances. Call for help the minute you see Dr. Prentice. (*Goes to the hall door, waving the gun. She goes into the hall.*)

(NICK *opens the strait jacket.* DR. PRENTICE *enters from the garden, carrying the dress taken from* MRS. PRENTICE.)

PRENTICE. Oh, there you are. Miss Barclay is nowhere to be found. Have you seen her? I want you to cooperate with me in getting things back to normal in this house.

MATCH. (*Enters from the garden swaying unsteadily.*) I'm ready to be examined when you are, Doctor. (*He stumbles into the wards. As he crosses,* PRENTICE *slaps his helmet on his head.*)

GERALDINE. (*Wearing* NICK'S *uniform, staggers in from the garden.*) They're combing the grounds for us, Doctor! They've got guns. What shall we do?

PRENTICE. It would help me considerably if you'd take your clothes off. You must lose no time in getting undressed. Both of you.

NICK. (*Pause.*) If I do that, sir, will you put this on? (*He holds up the jacket.*)

PRENTICE. (*Angry, losing patience.*) Of course not! That's a strait jacket. I won't be a party to kinky capers. You've lived too long at the Station Hotel to know how decent people behave. Now do as I say and undress!

GERALDINE. (*Tearful, beating him away.*) You're behaving like a maniac!

NICK. He is a maniac. He's murdered a woman and hidden her body somewhere.

PRENTICE. Who is responsible for these vile stories?

NICK. Dr. Rance is having you certified. (*Waving the jacket.*) I've got to get you into this! (*He leaps upon* DR. PRENTICE *and attempts to put him into the strait jacket.*)

MATCH. (*Enters from the wards—retreats immediately.*) I'm ready when you are, Doctor!

PRENTICE. (*To* NICK.) Put that down. Take your clothes off. Don't you know the penalty for impersonating a sergeant? Put on your own clothing. Give this youth that tunic and put on this dress and all our problems will be solved.

(NICK *takes off his uniform.* GERALDINE *pulls down her trousers.* NICK *is now naked except for his underpants.* GERALDINE *exits into wards.* MRS. PRENTICE *enters from the hall in her underwear, waving a gun. She advances on* DR. PRENTICE.)

MRS. PRENTICE. (*Waving gun at him.*) Come with me and lie down!

PRENTICE. The woman is insatiable.

MRS. PRENTICE. Unless you make love to me I shall shoot you.

PRENTICE. No husband can be expected to give his best at gun point. (*He backs away and exits into the garden. She shoots at him.*)

(*Hearing the shot,* NICK, *who has crouched behind the desk to hide from* MRS. PRENTICE, *runs into the hall. A SECOND SHOT.* GERALDINE *enters from the wards, sees* MRS. PRENTICE *and retreats back into the wards. THIRD SHOT.* MATCH *enters from wards, sees* MRS. PRENTICE *and exits running into the garden. FOURTH SHOT.* NICK *enters from the hall and exits running into the garden.* MRS. PRENTICE *follows after him, then re-enters immediately as* DR. RANCE *enters from the hall.*)

MRS. PRENTICE. Doctor Rance! Doctor Rance! The world is full of naked men running in all directions!

RANCE. When did these delusions start?

MRS. PRENTICE. Just now.

RANCE. It's not difficult to guess what's on your mind, my dear. Are you having marital troubles?

MRS. PRENTICE. Well, yes. My husband refuses to prescribe anything.

RANCE. A man shouldn't have to drug his wife to achieve a happy union.

MRS. PRENTICE. I don't want drugs. I want account taken of my sexual nature.

RANCE. Where do you keep your tranquilizers? (GERALDINE *runs out from the wards. She has taken off the uniform and wears her own panties and bra.*) At last we've caught the patient! Get the strait jacket! (*Takes one from the chair.*)

GERALDINE. I'm not a patient. I'm telling the truth!

RANCE. It's much too late to tell the truth. (*Ties* GERALDINE *down.*) These final harrowing scenes will be lavishly illustrated with graphs showing the effect of her downfall upon her poor tortured mind. Meanwhile, in his temple of love, the hideous Dr. Prentice and his acolyte are praying to their false gods, unaware that the forces of reason have got their measure. (MRS. PRENTICE *steps back.*) Fetch a syringe. (MRS. PRENTICE *goes into the wards.*)

GERALDINE. (*Trussed up, unable to move.*) What have I done to deserve this? I've always led such a respectable life.

RANCE. Where is the body?

GERALDINE. I don't know.

RANCE. Are you under the seal of the confessional? What black rites were you initiated into by that foul priest of the Unknown? (GERALDINE *sobs, unable to speak.* DR. RANCE *abruptly throws himself on to her and holds her in his arms.*) Let me cure your neurosis! It's the only thing I want out of life.

(MRS. PRENTICE *enters from the dispensary, carrying a hypodermic syringe and bowl.*)

MRS. PRENTICE. What is the meaning of this exhibition?

RANCE. (*Breaking away from* GERALDINE.) It's a new and hitherto untried type of therapy. I think it's viable under the circumstances.

MRS. PRENTICE. Your treatment seems designed to plunge the patient deeper into lunacy rather than achieve any lasting cure.

RANCE. Someone whose unconscious is as quirky as your own could hardly be expected to understand my methods.

MRS. PRENTICE. What do you mean by that?

RANCE. I'm referring to those naked men you encounter with an increasing degree of frequency.

MRS. PRENTICE. You've seen them too.

RANCE. What does that prove? Merely that you've given me your wretched disease. Give me that! (*He takes the hypodermic from her.*)

MRS. PRENTICE. Shouldn't I swab the patient's arm?

RANCE. You don't imagine I'm wasting this stuff on her, do you? (*He rolls back his sleeve.*) For what it costs an ounce, it would be criminal. (*He gives himself an injection.*) Go and call the police. (*Puts the hypodermic aside.*)

MRS. PRENTICE. There's a policeman outside, naked in the center of the garden.

RANCE. If he is, indeed, naked, how do you dare to presume he is a policeman?

MRS. PRENTICE. He's wearing his helmet.

RANCE. The bounds of decency have long been overstepped in this house. Your subconscious cannot be encouraged in its skulduggery. Remain where you are. I'll call the police. (RANCE *exits to wards.*)

(NICK *appears from the garden.*)

MRS. PRENTICE. Oh, I'm losing my mind!

GERALDINE. (*Calls to* NICK.) Help me!

NICK. Why are you tied up?

GERALDINE. Dr. Rance did it. He says I'm mad.

NICK. He's a psychiatrist, he must know. He wouldn't put you in a strait jacket if you were sane. He'd have to be mad.

GERALDINE. He is mad!

NICK. (*To* GERALDINE.) Is she mad?

GERALDINE. She thinks she is. She imagines you're a figment of her imagination.

NICK. (*To* MRS. PRENTICE, *nodding to* GERALDINE.) Mrs. Prentice, she can see me. Doesn't that prove I'm real?

MRS. PRENTICE. No. She's mad.

NICK. If you think I'm a phantom of your subconscious you must be mad.

PRENTICE. Why were you chasing me with a gun? Do you think I'm mad?

MRS. PRENTICE. (*With a hysterical giggle.*) I am mad! (NICK *grabs her gun.*)

PRENTICE. (*Entering from the garden as* DR. RANCE *is putting* MRS. PRENTICE *into a strait jacket.*) Are you all mad? Stop! A husband must be allowed to put his own wife into a strait jacket. It's one of the few pleasures left in modern marriage. (*Grabs gun from* NICK.) Stand away!

Doctor Rance! Your conduct today has been a model of official irresponsibility and I'm going to certify you.

RANCE. (*Quietly, with dignity.*) No. I am going to certify you.

PRENTICE. I have the weapon. You have the choice. What is it to be? Madness or death, neither of which would enable you to continue to be employed by the Government.

RANCE. That isn't true. The higher reaches of the civil service are recruited entirely from corpses or madmen. Your deterrent is useless. Put it down. (DR. RANCE *takes out his own gun and points it at the astonished* DR. PRENTICE. *Holding* DR. PRENTICE *at bay with the gun.*) I'll have you in a jacket within the hour.

PRENTICE. Is that a record for you?

RANCE. By no means. I once put a whole family into a communal strait jacket.

PRENTICE. How proud your mother must've been.

RANCE. She wasn't, I'm afraid. It was my own family, you see. I've a snapshot of the scene at home. My foot placed squarely upon my father's head. I sent it to Sigmund Freud and had a charming postcard in reply.

(SERGEANT MATCH *enters from the garden.*)

MATCH. (*To* RANCE.) I'm still ready to be examined, Doctor.

RANCE. (*To* PRENTICE, *in a firm voice.*) What have you done with Geradline Barclay?

GERALDINE. (*Feebly.*) I'm here.

MATCH. (*To* GERALDINE, *with all the dignity he can muster.*) Will you kindly produce, or cause to be produced, the missing part of Sir Winston Churchill?

PRENTICE. Stop! All of you! (*Grabs gun from* RANCE.) We are now approaching what our racier novelists term the climax. Release my wife and the young woman, too. The story you're about to hear is concerned solely with the heart: the mind and its mysteries could not have been further from my thoughts when, early this morning, in what must be the most ill-timed attempt at seduction ever, I persuaded that young woman to take her clothes off.

GERALDINE. (*To* DR. RANCE.) Mrs. Prentice mistook my dress for her own and, by an oversight, you mistook me for a patient. Dr. Prentice asked me to keep quiet in order to protect his good name. What could I do? I was terrified of exposure.

MRS. PRENTICE. You were naked at the time?

GERALDINE. Yes. Under duress I agreed to help the doctor. I've never ceased reproaching myself. The whole day has been spent fighting to retain my self-respect.

PRENTICE. Oh, if I live to be ninety, I'll never again attempt sexual intercourse.

RANCE. I'd be willing to stake my professional reputation upon the fact that this girl has been the victim of an incestuous attack. I won't go back upon my diagnosis. My publishers will sue me for loss of royalties.

GERALDINE. (*Stepping from the couch.*) I'm sure my shorthand speed has been affected by what I've suffered today. (*Tearful, to* DR. PRENTICE.) And I wish to report the loss of my lucky elephant charm.

RANCE. (*Takes a brooch from his pocket.*) Is this the piece of jewelry to which you refer? I removed it from your neck when I cut your hair.

GERALDINE. Yes. It has great sentimental value. (DR. RANCE *passes brooch to* MRS. PRENTICE *who gives it to* GERALDINE.)

NICK. Look. I've got one like that. (*Shows* GERALDINE *a brooch.*)

MRS. PRENTICE. A single brooch can be made of these two fragments. Oh, my heart is beating like a wild thing!

(DR. RANCE *examines the brooch.*)

NICK and GERALDINE. It's true!

MATCH. Two elephants carrying a richly engraved howdah in which is seated a young and beautiful woman —perhaps a princess of the royal line—magnificent example of oriental craftsmanship. (*To* MRS. PRENTICE.) How did you know this was a single piece?

MRS. PRENTICE. It belonged to me once. Many years ago, when I was a young woman, I was raped in a linen closet on the second floor of the Station Hotel. As the man left me he pressed that brooch into my hands in part payment.

MATCH. How did these children come to be in possession of the separate halves?

MRS. PRENTICE. I paid for my misdemeanor by conceiving twins. It was impossible for me to keep them—I was by then engaged to be married to a promising young psychiatrist. I decided to abandon them to their fate. I broke the brooch in half and pinned a separate piece to each babe. I then placed them at either end of the small country town in which I was resident. Some kind people must've brought the children up as their own. (*Hugging* NICK *and* GERALDINE.) Oh, children! I am your mother! Can you ever forgive me for what I did?

NICK. What kind of mother must you have been to stay alone at the Station Hotel?

MRS. PRENTICE. I was employed as a chambermaid. I did it for a joke shortly after the war. The effect of a Labour Government on the middle classes had to be seen to be believed.

GERALDINE. Was our father also employed by the Station Hotel?

MRS. PRENTICE. I never saw your father. The incident occurred during a power failure. I became pregnant as I waited for normal services to be resumed.

PRENTICE. You'll find an inscription on the back of the brooch, sir—"To Lillian from Avis. Christmas 1939." I found that brooch many years ago. It was on the pavement outside a large department store.

RANCE. Who were Lillian and Avis?

PRENTICE. I've no idea. It fell from the collar of a Pekinese. Lillian and Avis may have been the creature's owners. (*He stares about him in shame.*) I haven't seen it since I pressed it into the hand of a chambermaid whom I debauched shortly before my marriage.

MRS. PRENTICE. (*With a cry of recognition.*) I understand now why you suggested that we spend our wedding night in a linen closet!

PRENTICE. I wished to recreate a moment that was very precious to me. My darling, we have been instrumental in uncovering a number of remarkable peccadilloes today.

RANCE. (*To* PRENTICE, *with wild delight.*) If you are this child's father my book can be written in good faith—she *is* the victim of an incestuous attack!

MRS. PRENTICE. And so am I, doctor! My son has a collection of photographs which prove beyond doubt that he attempted to seduce me in the same hotel—indeed in the same linen closet where his conception took place.

RANCE. Double incest is even more likely to produce a best-seller than murder—and this is as it should be for love must bring greater joy than violence.

DR. PRENTICE. Come, let us put on our clothes and face the world. (*They all turn to the audience and bow crisply and formally.*)

BLACKOUT

THE CURTAIN FALLS

PROPERTY PLOT

Off Stage—*down right:*

2 differently-shaped tumblers
1 straitjacket (worn by Mrs. Prentice)
Paper towels
1 kidney-shaped basin
1 hospital trolley with loose sheet for cover
Geraldine's hospital gown
Nick's gray pumps

Off Stage—*down left:*

Sgt. Match's aubergine dress
Mrs. Prentice' shocking pink dress
2 hospital coats (Dr. Prentice and Dr. Rance) with red pill-box in the pocket of Dr. Rance's

Off Stage—*up right:*

1 black attaché case (Dr. Rance) with monograph and pad inside
1 medical magazine
5 envelopes, 3 white and 2 colored, all addressed
1 hooded aubergine dress on wooden hanger (Nicholas Beckett)
2 straitjackets (Geraldine and Nick)

Off Stage—*up left:*

1 brass, medium-size, oriental-type vase with bright red artificial roses in it
1 medium-sized syringe with needle (blunted) attached

On-Stage Props:

On top of cabinet, far right:

1 stethoscope; 1 pair rubber gloves; 1 reflex hammer; 1 small paper cup filled with water; 1 plastic pill bottle; 1 silver decanter

Stage-right table:

1 large vase with red cloth red roses; 2 medical (psychi·atric) magazines

On top of desk, stage left:

1 pencil holder with many pencils; scissors and letter opener combination; 1 bottle man's cologne; 1 dictaphone microphone; pen in holder; 1 desk pad

Inside desk drawers, top right:
1 white pillbox; top left: 1 committal order form; bottom left: two small guns (props only).

On top of cabinet, far left:
1 silver decanter, two small glasses; 3 water tumblers, 1 decanter half-filled with liquor

Upstage behind curtains:
identical bra and panties to Geraldine's; 1 stand-by note (the one Dr. Prentice throws to Geraldine)

NOTE: The cabinets, right and left, are dressed with several medical jars filled with wooden swabs, gauze pads, cotton balls, etc. The bookcases right and left are filled with matching sets of books. The stage-right bookcase contains 1 large, available, leather-type bound volume. The bookcase stage-left contains a leather-bound clippings file. The stage-right table is dressed with 1 elegant, sterling silver cigarette box and 1 conical, covered sterling silver jar.

COSTUME PLOT

DR. PRENTICE:

Three-piece oxford-gray, pin-striped, well-tailored, single-breasted suit; black shoes and socks; black and white striped shirt; white and gray print tie; a below-the-knee white hospital coat.

MRS. PRENTICE:

A simply cut white coat with rhinestone brooch at the neck; a shocking-pink, box-pleated dress; blue and white chemise with matching panties; dark-shade panty hose; bone-color shoes (simple pumps) with onyx buckle; black, wrist-length gloves.

GERALDINE BARCLAY:

Same dress as Mrs. Prentice; bright orange bra; bikini-cut, bright floral panties; light-shade panty hose; gray cloth sling pumps; gray purse; short white gloves; a white hospital gown (as are worn by patients).
sling pumps; gray purse; short white gloves; a white hospital gown (as are worn by patients).

DR. RANCE

Three-piece, dark brown, glen-plaid, single-breasted suit; tan and white striped shirt with matching bow tie; brown Bass-type, rubber-soled shoes; suspenders; brown and beige argyle socks; a hospital coat identical to the one Dr. Prentice wears.

SERGEANT MATCH

Modified bobby's uniform—tunic top—sergeant stripes on sleeve; policeman's helmet; black boots; suspenders; long black socks; garters; pale green, plaid boxer shorts; sleeveless undershirt; hooded, jersey aubergine dress.

NICHOLAS BECKETT

Bright red gold-trimmed page boy's uniform with short jacket, gold buttons, with matching pillbox hat; black patent-leather shoes; black socks; red boxer shorts; identical pumps to Geraldine Barclay's; hooded, jersey, aubergine dress.

One prop dress to look like the shocking-pink ones which Mrs. Prentice and Geraldine Barclay wear.

SOUND PLOT

GUN SHOTS:
Need two practical 22 blank pistols (one as cover gun). USED OFF STAGE ONLY!

BUZZER:
With a harsh sound, e.g., hockey game buzzer.

FIRE GONG OR SIREN:
Both are easily purchasable in burglar alarm supply stores. Operated manually by stage manager. Rigged with push buttons and can be plugged into 110 volt wall socket.

LIGHT PLOT

GENERAL AREA ILLUMINATION. VERY BRIGHT. GLOW FROM ABOVE DOME AREA IF USED.

NO INTERNAL LIGHT CUES. LIGHTS BUMP UP BRIGHTLY AT THE OPENING OF EACH ACT AND BLACKOUT AT THE END OF EACH ACT.

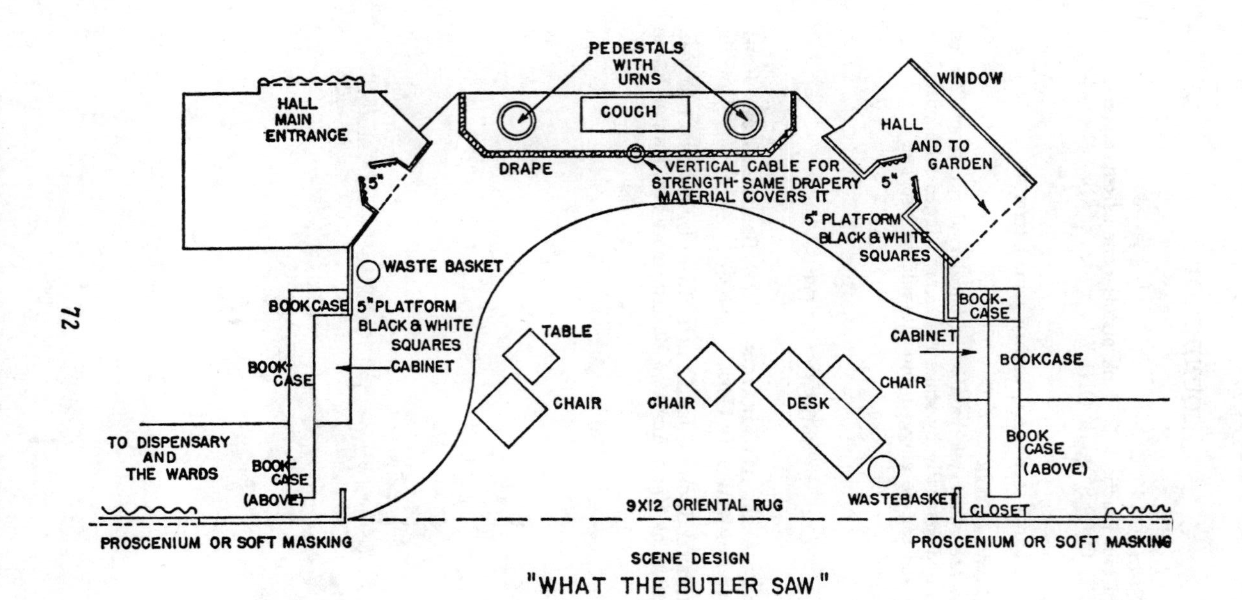

SCENE DESIGN
"WHAT THE BUTLER SAW"